WORKED EXAMPLES

HIGHER

MATHEMATICS

Paper 1

(Non-Calculator Paper)

by

M. Kyle

ISBN 0 7169 3253 9

ROBERT GIBSON · Publisher
17 Fitzroy Place, Glasgow, G3 7SF, Scotland, U.K.

INTRODUCTION

This book is designed for pupils to use independently as revision exercises for the Higher Still non-calculator paper. The twelve papers enclosed contain questions similar to the type of questions in Paper 1 of the Higher examination. The content includes trigonometry (with special angles), calculus, completing the square, recurrence relations and log graphs. Emphasis is placed on graph sketching in several topics.

The content is also relevant to the internal learning outcome assessments, and should prove helpful in the preparation for these class exams.

ANALYSIS OF CONTENTS

Paper	A	B	C	D	E	F	G	H	I	J	K	L
Geometry												
The straight line		1	4,10	7	7	3	3,12	3		2,3	2	2,7
Circle	3	3	3		4	4	4	5	3	12	10	
Vectors	11	2	7	8	1	2	10	9	11	1	12	12
Algebra												
Quadratics	5	10	8	11	5	10		8	12	8,10	4	10
Functions $f(g(x))$	6	9		10					9		6	
Polynomials	12	7	6		8	1,8		2,7	1,8			5,6
Recurrence	7	11	9	9		9	6	10		7		8
Logs								6			11	
Curve sketching			1	3				4	10			
Calculus												
Sketching $f'(x)$	4	6	5		11		9				7	
Differentiation	8	4	2	12	10	5,7	7		7	4,9	1	11
Integration	9	8	12	2	2	11	11	1		6	8	
Trig differentiation					6				5		9	
Trigonometry												
Max-Min				6	12		8	11				3
Graph sketching	1			4	3		2					9
Addition formula	2	12	11		9		5		2	11	3	
Trig equations						12		12				4
Angle of gradient				5,12								
R cos x / R sin x				1		6	1		4,6			
Standard Grade	10	5								5	5	1

3

FORMULAE LIST

Circle:

The equation $x^2 + y^2 + 2gx + 2fy + c = 0$ represents a circle centre $(-g, -f)$ and radius $\sqrt{g^2 + f^2 - c}$.

The equation $(x - a)^2 + (y - b)^2 = r^2$ represents a circle centre (a, b) and radius r.

Scalar Product:

$a.b = |a|\,|b|\cos\theta$, where θ is the angle between a and b

or $\quad a.b = a_1 b_1 + a_2 b_2 + a_3 b_3$ where $a = \begin{pmatrix} a_1 \\ a_2 \\ a_3 \end{pmatrix}$ and $b = \begin{pmatrix} b_1 \\ b_2 \\ b_3 \end{pmatrix}$.

Trigonometric formulae:

$$\sin(A \pm B) = \sin A \cos B \pm \cos A \sin B$$
$$\cos(A \pm B) = \cos A \cos B \mp \sin A \sin B$$
$$\sin 2A = 2\sin A \cos A$$
$$\cos 2A = \cos^2 A - \sin^2 A = 2\cos^2 A - 1 = 1 - 2\sin^2 A$$

Table of standard derivatives and integrals:

$f(x)$	$f'(x)$
$\sin ax$	$a\cos ax$
$\cos ax$	$-a\sin ax$

$f(x)$	$\int f(x)\,dx$
$\sin ax$	$-\dfrac{1}{a}\cos ax + C$
$\cos ax$	$\dfrac{1}{a}\sin ax + C$

TEST PAPER A

1. In how many places does the graph of $f : x \rightarrow \cos 3x$ cross the x-axis, $0 \leq x < 360$?

   Draw a rough sketch to illustrate your answer.

2. In a right angled triangle $\tan A = \frac{5}{3}$,

   find

   (a) the exact value of $\cos 2A$

   (b) and show that $\cos 2A + \sin 2A = \frac{7}{17}$.

3. A circle with equation $x^2 + y^2 - 8x + 11 = 0$ touches another circle at the point $(6, 1)$. Find the equation of this second circle if its radius is twice as long.

4. In the graph shown, for what values of x are the statements $f(x) > 0$ and $f'(x) < 0$ both true.

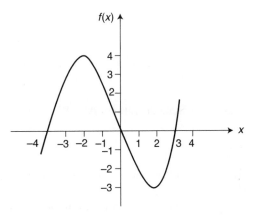

5. (a) Using the method of completing the square find the minimum value of $y = x^2 - 6x + 4$.

   (b) Make a rough sketch of the curve showing the turning point and any axis intercepts.

   (c) From your sketch state the nature of the roots of the equation giving an explanation.

6. $f(x) = x^2 - 3$ and $g(x) = 2x + 1$

   (a) Find $f(g(x))$ and $g(f(x))$.

   (b) If $f(g(x)) - g(f(x)) = 9$, find the possible values of x.

7. A sequence is defined by the recurrence relation $u_{n+1} = 2u_n + 3$

   (a) Express u_{n+2} in terms of u_n.

   (b) If $u_{n+3} = 53$, find the value of u_n.

   (c) Find u_{n-1} and u_{n+4}, using the value of u_n from (b).

8. When $f(x) = (x^2 - 3x)^3$, find $f'(x)$ and $f'(-1)$.

9. If $\int_a^3 (3x^2 - 2x)\,dx = 20$, find a.

10. A chord AB is 3 units from the centre of a circle centre O and radius 5.

Find $\sin A\hat{O}B$.

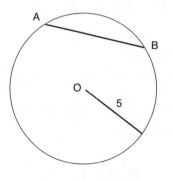

11. *(a)* A is the point $(3, 1, 4)$, B is the point $(6, 7, 10)$. P divides AB in the ratio $1 : 2$. Find the coordinates of P.

(b) State the ratio of AP : BP.

12. *(a)* Given that $(x + 3)$ is a factor of $f(x) = x^3 + 6x^2 + 5x - 12$, fully factorise $f(x)$.

(b) State the coordinates of the points where $f(x)$ meets the axes.

TEST PAPER B

1. The vertices of a triangle are P(2, –1), Q(3, 2) and R(6, 5).

   Find the equation of the altitude AQ.

2. P = (2, a, –3), Q = (1, a, a). If OP is perpendicular to OQ, find the value of a.

3. *(a)* Find the coordinates of the centre and the length of the radius of the circle with equation

   $$x^2 + y^2 - 4x + 2y + 1 = 0.$$

   (b) Find the equation of this circle reflected in the x-axis.

4. Stationary values of the function $x^3 + mx$ occur when $x = \pm 1$. Find the value of m.

5. Find the value of $(\sqrt{3} + 2\sqrt{2})^2$.

6. The graph shown is $f(x)$.

   Make a rough sketch of $f'(x)$.

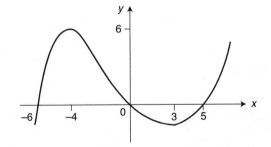

7. If the function $3x^3 - 16x^2 + px + 10$ is divisible by $(x - 1)$, find p and fully factorise the function.

8. If $f'(x) = 3x - 2$ and $f(2) = 7$, find $f(x)$.

9. If $f(x) = 2x^2$ and $g(x) = 3x - 1$, find $f(g(x))$.

10. *(a)* Show that the function $3x^2 - 4x + 2$ has no real roots.

(b) Show by completing the square that the function $3x^2 - 4x + 2$ has minimum value $\dfrac{2}{3}$.

(c) Make a rough sketch of the function.

11. *(a)* If $u_{r+1} = mu_r + c$ and $u_0 = 1$, $u_1 = -3$ and $u_2 = 21$, find m and c and state the relationship in the form $u_{r+1} = mu_r + c$.

(b) Find u_3 and u_{-1}.

(c) Find a value for u_r such that $u_{r+1} = u_r$.

12. If $\sin x = \dfrac{2}{5}$ $(0 < x < 90)$, find the **exact** values of $\sin 2x$ and $\cos 2x$.

TEST PAPER C

1. Find the coordinates of A, B and C when the equation of the curve is $y = 5\log_2(2x + 2)$ and the equation of the line is $y = 10$.

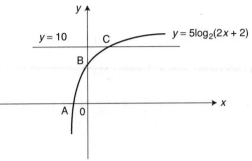

2. Stationary values of the function $2x^3 + mx$ occur when $x = \pm 2$. Find the value of m. Hence state $f(x)$ and $f(-1)$.

3. (a) Find the coordinates of the centre and the length of the radius of the circle with equation

$$x^2 + y^2 - 2x + 6y + 1 = 0.$$

   (b) State the equation of the circle after reflection in the y-axis.

4. The vertices of a triangle are A$(-1, 3)$, B$(2, -1)$ and C$(5, 4)$.

   Find the equation of the altitude BQ.

5. The graph of $f(x)$ is shown.

   Make a rough sketch of $f'(x)$.

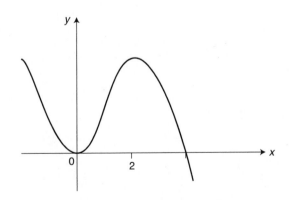

6. (a) Given that $(x + 1)$ is a factor of $f(x) = x^3 + 3x^2 - 13x - 15$, fully factorise $f(x)$.

   (b) State the coordinates of the points where $f(x)$ meets the axes.

7. *(a)* A is the point $(2, -1, 3)$, B is the point $(1, 6, -4)$. P divides AB in the ratio $2 : -3$. Find the coordinates of P.

(b) State the ratios AB : PB and AB : BP.

8. *(a)* Using the method of completing the square, find the minimum value of $y = x^2 + 4x + 11$.

(b) Make a rough sketch of the curve showing the turning point and any axis intercepts.

(c) From your sketch, state the nature of the roots of the equation, giving an explanation.

9. A certain sequence of numbers is defined by the recurrence relation $u_{n+1} = 0{\cdot}4u_n + 12$.

Explain why this sequence has a limit and find the limit of the sequence.

10. If the points $(1, 2)$, $(a, 4)$ and $(b, 1)$ are collinear, show that $a + 2b = 3$.

11. If $\tan x = \dfrac{5}{12}$, $\tan y = \dfrac{3}{4}$. Show that $\cos(x - y) - \sin(x + y) = \dfrac{7}{65}$.

12. If $\displaystyle\int_{b}^{2}(3x^2 - 2)\,dx = 3$, find b.

TEST PAPER D

1. In a right angled triangle $\tan A = \dfrac{3}{2}$, show that $\cos A$ can be expressed in the form $p\sqrt{13}$ and state the exact value of p.

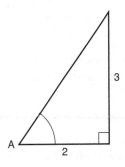

2. When $f(x) = \sin^3 x + \cos^2 x$, find $f'(x)$ and $f'\left(\dfrac{\pi}{4}\right)$. (Leave your answer in surd form.)

3. The graph shown is $f(x)$. Sketch $-f(x)$ and $f(x) + 1$ on separate graphs.

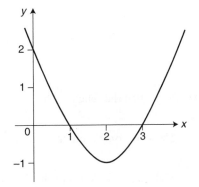

4. (a) In how many places does the graph of $f : x \rightarrow \sin 4x$ cross the x-axis, $0 \le x \le 360$?

   (b) Sketch the graph to illustrate your answer.

5. (a) Find the equation of the line through $(0, -1)$ which makes an angle of $45°$ with the x-axis.

   (b) State the equation of the line which is perpendicular to this line and passes through the point $(1, 3)$.

   (c) State the y-intercept of this perpendicular line and the angle which it makes with the x-axis.

6. (a) $A = 3 \cos\left(x - \dfrac{\pi}{6}\right) \qquad 0 \le x \le 2\pi$
   Find the maximum and minimum values of A.

   (b) State the coordinates of the turning points.

11

7. A triangle has coordinates $(1, 2)$, $(-3, 4)$ and $(5, 6)$ respectively.

Find the coordinates of the centroid of the triangle.

8. P is the point $(2, -1, 3)$ relative to rectangular axes OX, OY and OZ. Find the cosine of angle POX. (Leave your answer as a surd.)

9. *(a)* If $u_{r+1} = mu_r + c$, find m and c and state the relationship in the form $u_{r+1} = mu_r + c$ when $u_0 = -1$, $u_1 = 7$ and $u_2 = -9$.

(b) Find u_3 and u_{-1}.

(c) Find a value for u_r such that $u_{r+1} = u_r$.

10. If $g(x) = 3 - x^2$ and $f(x) = 1 - 2x$, find $g(f(x))$.

11. *(a)* Show that the function $3x^2 - 2x + 5$ has no real roots.

(b) Show by completing the square that the function $3x^2 - 2x + 5$ has minimum value $\dfrac{14}{3}$.

(c) Make a rough sketch of the function.

12. *(a)* Find the equation of the tangent to the curve $y = x^3 + 2x^2 - 4$ at the point where $x = -1$.

(b) Find the size of the angle between the tangent and the positive direction of the x-axis.

TEST PAPER E

1. $A = (4, -1, 5), C = (-1, 4, 10)$

   B is a point which divides AC in the ratio 2 : 3.

   Find the coordinates of B.

   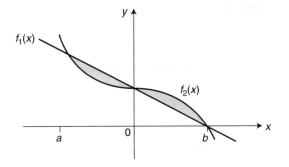

2. Write down an expression for the total shaded area as the sum of two integrals.

   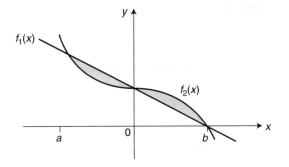

3. In how many places does the graph of $f : x \rightarrow \sin 3x$ cross the x-axis, $0 \le x < 360$?

   Draw a rough sketch to illustrate your answer.

4. A circle has equation $x^2 + y^2 - 8x + 6y + 21 = 0$. Find the equation of the circle under reflection in the y-axis.

5. *(a)* Using the method of completing the square, find the minimum value of $y = 1 + 2x - x^2$.

   (b) Make a rough sketch of the curve, showing the turning point and any axis intercepts.

   (c) From your sketch, state the nature of the roots of the equation, giving an explanation.

6. Find $f'\left(\dfrac{\pi}{4}\right)$ if $f(x) = 2 \sin 3x$.

7. A triangle has coordinates $P(1, 2), Q(6, 3)$ and $R(5, -2)$ respectively.

   (a) Find C the coordinates of the centroid of the triangle.

   (b) Find the mid-points M of PR and N of QP and the ratios QC : QM and RC : CN.

13

8. Factorise $x^3 - 3x^2 - 4x + 12$.

9. In a right-angled triangle, $\tan A = \dfrac{3}{7}$. Find the exact value of $\cos 2A$.

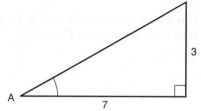

10. When $f(x) = (2x^2 - x)^5$, find $f'(x)$.

11. $f(x)$ is shown in the diagram.

Make a rough sketch of $f'(x)$.

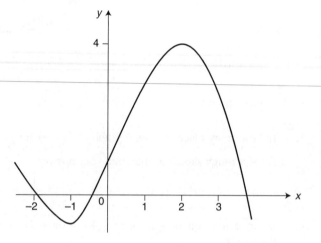

12. $C = 3 \cos \left(x + \dfrac{\pi}{3} \right)$ $0 \le x \le 2\pi$.

Find the maximum and minimum values of C and the corresponding values of x.

TEST PAPER F

1. *(a)* Given that $(x + 2)$ is a factor of $f(x) = x^3 - 3x^2 - 6x + 8$, fully factorise $f(x)$.

   (b) State the coordinates of the points where $f(x)$ meets the axes.
   (To show that $(x + 2)$ is a factor of $f(x)$ show that $f(-2) = 0$ and factorise the function fully.)

2. *(a)* A is the point $(1, -2, 4)$, B is the point $(-2, 4, 1)$. P divides AB in the ratio $2 : 1$. Find the coordinates of P.

   (b) State the ratio AP : BP.

3. The vertices of a triangle are L$(2, 4)$, M$(-1, -2)$ and N$(3, 7)$. Find the equation of the altitude LQ.

4. *(a)* Find the coordinates of the centre and the length of the radius of the circle with equation
   $$x^2 + y^2 - 6x + 8y + 9 = 0.$$

   (b) Find the equation of this circle after reflection in the x-axis.

5. Stationary values of the function $4x^3 + mx$ occur when $x = \pm \dfrac{\sqrt{3}}{2}$

   (a) Find the value of m.

   (b) State $f(x)$ and find $f(-2)$.

6. Find the value of $(2\sqrt{3} - 5\sqrt{2})^2$.

7. If $f(x) = \dfrac{x^3 + 2x^2 - 3x - 1}{3x^2}$ find $f'(x)$.

8. $f(x) = x^3 - 5x^2 - x + d$. If $f(x)$ is divisible by $(x + 1)$, find d and fully factorise the function.

9. (a) If $u_{r+1} = mu_r + c$ and $u_0 = 3$, $u_1 = 2$ and $u_2 = 4$, find m and c and state the relationship in the form $u_{r+1} = mu_r + c$.

(b) Find u_3 and u_{-1}.

(c) Find a value for u_r such that $u_{r+1} = u_r$.

10. (a) Find the value of p if $f(x) = 2x^2 + 6x + p$ has equal roots.

(b) State the coordinates of this root.

(c) Make a rough sketch of the curve showing clearly where $f(x)$ meets the axes.

11. Evaluate $\displaystyle\int_{\pi/3}^{\pi/2} \sin x \, dx.$

12. Solve $4 \sin 2x - 2 = 0; \quad 0 < x < 360.$

TEST PAPER G

1. Find the value of $(5 + 2\sqrt{3})^2$.

2. In how many places does the graph of $f : x \rightarrow \cos 4x$ cross the x-axis, $0 \le x \le 180$?
   Draw a rough sketch to illustrate your answer.

3. If the points A(2, 1), B(a, 5) and C(b, –7) are collinear, show that $2a + b = 6$.

4. A circle has equation $x^2 + y^2 - 8x + 6y + 21 = 0$. Find the equation of the circle under reflection in the line $y = -x$.

5. In a right-angled triangle, $\tan A = \dfrac{1}{2\sqrt{2}}$, find the exact value of $\cos 2A$ and $\sin 2A$.

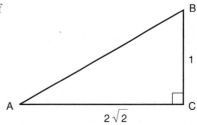

6. A sequence is defined by the recurrence relation $u_{n+1} = 4u_n - 5$.
   (a) Express u_{n+2} in terms of u_n.
   (b) If $u_{n+3} = 87$, find the value of u_n.
   (c) Find u_{n-1} and u_{n+4}.

7. When $f(x) = (3x^2 - 2x)^4$, find $f'(x)$ and $f'(-1)$.

8. $D = 2 \cos \left(x - \dfrac{\pi}{2} \right)$, $0 \le x \le 2\pi$

   Find the maximum and minimum values of D and the values of x at these points.

9. The diagram shows the sketch of $f(x)$.

Make a rough sketch of $f'(x)$.

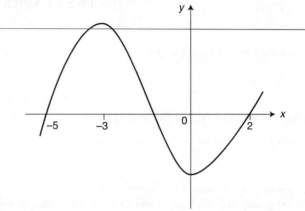

10. *(a)* A is the point $(2, -2, 5)$, B is the point $(-2, 2, -3)$, P divides AB in the ratio $1 : 3$. Find the coordinates of P.

(b) State the ratio AB : PB.

11. Given $f'(x) = 3x^2 - 4x + 5$ and the point $(-2, 6)$ lies on $f(x)$, find $f(3)$.

12. A triangle has coordinates $(2, 5)$, $(4, 1)$ and $(8, -3)$ respectively. Find the coordinates of the centroid of the triangle.

TEST PAPER H

1. If $\displaystyle\int_a^2 (x^2 - 1)\,dx = 0$, find a.

2. Find all the roots of the equation:

$$f(x) = x(x^2 - 3)(x^2 + 4)(x^2 - 1),\ x \in R.$$

State the answer in a solution set.

3. The vertices of a triangle are P(–2, 5), Q(2, –1) and R(4, 2). Find the equation of the altitude AQ.

4. Give two reasons why this graph cannot be the graph of $f(x) = 6 + x - x^2$.

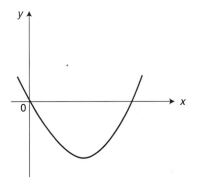

5. Find the coordinates of the centre and length of the radius of the circle with equation:

$$x^2 + y^2 + 12x - 4y + 15 = 0.$$

6. Simplify and evaluate $\log_{10}40 + \log_{10}20 - \log_{10}80$.

7. If $x^3 - 3x^2 - x + a$ is divisible by $(x - 3)$, find a.

8. $f(x) = 3x^2 - 2x - c$. Find the value of c if the function has equal roots.

9. P = (1, 4, –1), Q = (1, –2, 3). Find the cosine of angle POQ.

10. *(a)* If $u_{r+1} = mu_r + c$ and $u_0 = 2$, $u_1 = -1$ and $u_2 = 14$, find m and c and state the relationship in the form $u_{r+1} = mu_r + c$.

(b) Find u_3 and u_{-1}.

(c) Find a value for u_r such that $u_{r+1} = u_r$.

11. Find the coordinates of the maximum and minimum turning points of the equation $f(x) = 3\sin(2x + 30°)$ where $0 \le x \le 360$.

12. Solve $2\sin 2x + 1 = 0$, $\quad 0 < x < 360$.

TEST PAPER I

1. If $x^3 + 4x^2 + x - t$ is divisible by $(x + 2)$, find t and fully factorise the function.

2. If $\tan A = K$, prove that the exact value of $\cos 2A = \dfrac{1 - K^2}{1 + K^2}$

3. A circle has equation $x^2 + y^2 - 6x + 8y = 0$.

   (a) State the centre and radius of the circle.

   (b) Find the equation of the circle under reflection in the y-axis.

4. Solve for x: $\dfrac{2 + x}{2} - (2 - x) < 5$.

5. Find $f'\left(\dfrac{\pi}{6}\right)$ if $f(x) = 3 \sin 2x$.

6. In a right-angled triangle $\tan A = \dfrac{1}{2}$, show that $\cos A$ can be expressed in the form $p\sqrt{5}$ and state the exact value of p.

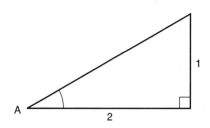

7. When $f(x) = (2x + \sqrt{x})^3$, find $f'(x)$ and $f'(4)$.

8. Find all the roots of the equation

   $$x(x + 2)(x^2 - 3)(x^2 + 1)(x^2 - 4), x \in R.$$

   State the answer in a solution set.

9. If $h(x) = g(f(x))$, find $h(x)$ when $f(x) = 2x - 1$ and $g(x) = -x^2 + x + 2$.

10. The diagram shows the sketch of the function $f(x)$. Make a rough sketch of $-f(x)$ and $f(x) - 2$ (on two different sketches).

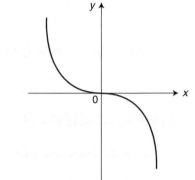

11. Given A = (−2, 3, 4), B = (−1, 5, 2) and C = (0, 1, 5), show that the cosine of angle BAC $= \dfrac{-4}{9}$ and comment on the type of angle.

12. *(a)* Using the method of completing the square, find the minimum value of $y = 3x^2 - 6x + 5$.

(b) Make a rough sketch of the curve showing the turning point and any axis intercepts.

(c) From your sketch, state the nature of the roots of the equation, giving an explanation.

TEST PAPER J

1. A is the point $(3, 1, 3)$, B is the point $(-2, 2, -2)$. P divides AB in the ratio $2 : 3$. Find the coordinates of P.

2. The vertices of a triangle are $P(2, 7)$, $Q(0, -1)$ and $R(-5, 4)$. Find the equation of the altitude AR.

3. If the points $(1, -1)$, $(a, 2)$ and $(b, 1)$ are collinear, show that $3b - 2a = 1$.

4. Stationary values of the function $4x^3 + mx$ occur when $x = \pm\dfrac{3}{2}$. Find the value of m.

5. Find the value of $(2\sqrt{3} + 3\sqrt{2})^2$.

6. Give an expression for the total sum of the shaded areas as the sum of two integrals.

    curve $= f_2(x)$
    line $\;= f_1(x)$

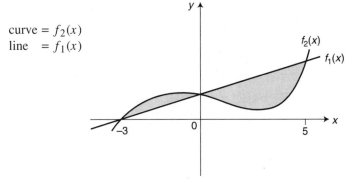

7. A sequence is given by the recurrence relation $u_{r+1} = ku_r + t$.

    (a) Find k and t if $u_0 = 0$, $u_1 = 2$ and $u_2 = -4$.

    (b) Find u_4 and u_{-1}.

8. Show by completing the square that the function $4x^2 + 4x + 5$ has minimum value 4.

9. Find the equation of the tangent to the curve $y = 3x^2 - 2x + 1$ which is parallel to the line with equation $y = x - 3$.

23

10. $f(x) = 2x^2 - bx + 3$. Find the value of b if the function

    (a)   has equal roots

    (b)   has real roots

    (c)   has no real roots.

    (d)   Make a sketch for each case.

11. In a right-angled triangle $\sin A = \dfrac{2}{3}$. Show that the exact value of $\tan 2A = 4\sqrt{5}$.

12. *(a)* Find the centre of the circle $x^2 + y^2 - 10x + 2y + 1 = 0$.

    (b)   Find the equation of the tangent to this circle through the point $Q(1, 2)$ on the circle.

    (c)   Find the coordinates of the points where the tangent meets the axes.

TEST PAPER K

1. For what values of x is the function $x^3 - 3x - 5$ decreasing? Make a rough sketch to illustrate your answer.

2. If P and Q are points on the curve $3xy = -2$ with x coordinates 1 and -1 respectively, find the gradient of PQ.

3. By expressing $3x$ as $(2x + x)$ and x as $(2x - x)$, find $\cos(3x) + \cos x$.

4. By the method of completing the square, find the minimum value of $2x^2 + x + 2$.

5. If $\dfrac{x - 2y}{3} = \dfrac{y - 2x}{2}$, find the value of $\dfrac{7x - 2y}{3x + y}$.

6. If $f(x) = x^2 - 3$ and $g(x) = 2 - x$, find $f(g(2))$.

7. The sketch shows the function $f(x)$.

   Make a rough sketch of $f'(x)$.

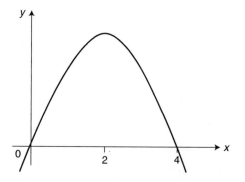

8. Evaluate $\displaystyle\int_1^4 \left(\sqrt{x} + \dfrac{1}{2\sqrt{x}} \right) dx$.

9. Find $f'\left(\dfrac{\pi}{2}\right)$ if $f(x) = 2\cos 3x$.

10. A circle has equation $x^2 + y^2 - 6x + 8y = 0$.

    Find the equation of the circle under reflection in the x-axis.

11. Find the coordinates of A, B and C when the equation of the curve is $y = 2\log_5(2x + 5)$ and the equation of the line is $y = 4$.

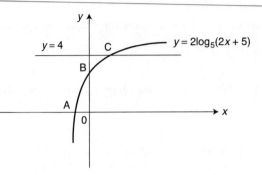

12. Given A = (3, –1, 0), B = (2, 0, 1) and C = (1, 1, –1), show that angle ABC = 90°.

TEST PAPER L

1. If $\dfrac{x^2 + 100}{x + 10} = x - 10 + \dfrac{k}{x + 10}$, find k.

2. If the points $(3, -1)$, $(a, 2)$ and $(b, 5)$ are collinear, show that $2a - b = 3$.

3. $K = 3 \cos \left(3x - \dfrac{\pi}{2}\right)$, $\quad 0 \le x \le 2\pi$.

   Find the maximum and minimum values of D and the values of x where these occur.

4. Solve $2 \cos 2x - 1 = 0$, $\quad 0 < x < 360$.

5. $f(x) = x(x^2 + 4)(x^2 - 3)(x^2 - 1)$, $x \in R$.

   Find the number of values of x for which $f(x) = 0$.

   State these values in a solution set.

6. If $x^3 + 3x^2 - 4x + q$ is divisible by $(x - 2)$, find the value of q.

7. The vertices of a triangle are $P(-1, 5)$, $Q(-3, 2)$ and $R(9, -1)$. Find the equation of the altitude AP.

8. (a) $u_{r+1} = ku_r + t$. Find k and t if $u_0 = 2$, $u_1 = -2$ and $u_2 = 10$.

   (b) Find the value of u_r such that $u_{r+1} = u_r$.

9. Sketch the graph of $f(x) = 3 \cos 2x$ for $0 \le x \le 2\pi$.
   Show clearly the maximum and minimum values and the x-, y-intercepts.

10. $f(x) = ax^2 + 4x - 2$. Find the value of a if the function

    (a)   has equal roots

    (b)   has real roots

    (c)   has no real roots.

    (d)   Make a sketch for each case.

11.   *(a)*   Find the equation of the tangent to the curve $y = x^3 - 4x^2 + 2x$ at the point where $x = 1$.

    (b)   Find the coordinates of the points where the tangent meets the axes.

12.   Given $A = (-1, 4, -2)$, $B = (1, 2, -3)$ and $C = (0, 3, -4)$,

     show that the cosine of angle $BAC = \dfrac{2}{\sqrt{6}}$

     and comment on the type of angle.

WORKED EXAMPLE — TEST PAPER A

1. $f(x) = \cos 3x, \{0 \le x < 360\}$

Consider the pattern of $\cos x$ which repeats every $360°$.

The period of $\cos x$ is $360°$.

The period of $\cos 3x$ is $\dfrac{360°}{3} = 120°$.

Hence the pattern repeats every $120°$, almost 3 complete patterns occur within the given set $\{0 \le x < 360\}$.

x	0	30	60	90	120	150	180	210	240	270	300	330
$3x$	0	90	180	270	360	450	540	630	720	810	900	990
$\cos 3x$	1	0	-1	0	1	0	-1	0	1	0	-1	0

Points on the graph $(x, \cos 3x)$ are $(0°, 1)$ $(30°, 0)$ $(60°, -1)$ $(90°, 0)$ $(120°, 1)$ $(150°, 0)$, etc., as seen in the above table.

Hence the graph of $\cos 3x$ cuts the x-axis in 6 places namely $(30°, 0)$ $(90°, 0)$ $(150°, 0)$ $(210°, 0)$ $(270°, 0)$ $(330°, 0)$.

Graph of $\cos 3x$.

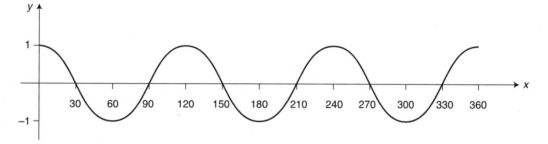

2. *(a)* $\operatorname{Tan} A = \dfrac{5}{3}$ → sketch and label a right angled triangle

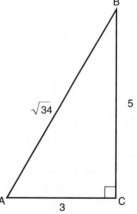

Using the theorem of Pythagoras to find the 3rd side,
$$AB^2 = AC^2 + BC^2$$
$$= 5^2 + 3^2$$
$$AB^2 = 34$$
$$AB = \sqrt{34}$$

Using the ratio of right angled triangles

$$\cos A = \frac{3}{\sqrt{34}} \qquad \sin A = \frac{5}{\sqrt{34}}$$

$\cos 2A$ Using double angle Trig. formula

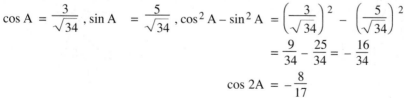

$$\cos 2A = \cos A \cos A - \sin A \sin A$$
$$= \cos^2 A - \sin^2 A$$

$$\cos A = \frac{3}{\sqrt{34}}, \sin A = \frac{5}{\sqrt{34}}, \cos^2 A - \sin^2 A = \left(\frac{3}{\sqrt{34}}\right)^2 - \left(\frac{5}{\sqrt{34}}\right)^2$$

$$= \frac{9}{34} - \frac{25}{34} = -\frac{16}{34}$$

$$\cos 2A = -\frac{8}{17}$$

OR using

$$\cos^2 A - \sin^2 A$$
$$= \cos^2 A - (1 - \sin^2 A)$$
$$= 2\cos^2 A - 1$$

$\cos A = \dfrac{3}{\sqrt{34}}$, $\quad = 2\left(\dfrac{3}{\sqrt{34}}\right)^2 - 1$

$$= 2\left(\dfrac{9}{34}\right) - 1 = \dfrac{9}{17} - \dfrac{17}{17}$$

$\cos 2A = -\dfrac{8}{17}$

(b) To show $\cos 2A + \sin 2A = \dfrac{7}{17}$

$\cos 2A = -\dfrac{8}{17}$ as found in part *(a)*.

By double angle formula $\sin 2A = \sin(A + A)$
$$= \sin A \cos A + \cos A \sin A$$
$$= 2 \sin A \cos A$$

$\cos A = \dfrac{3}{\sqrt{34}}$, $\sin A = \dfrac{5}{\sqrt{34}}$,

$\Rightarrow 2 \sin A \cos A = 2\left(\dfrac{5}{\sqrt{34}}\right)\left(\dfrac{3}{\sqrt{34}}\right)$

$$= \dfrac{30}{34}$$

$\sin 2A = \dfrac{15}{17}$, and from part *(a)* $\cos 2A = -\dfrac{8}{17}$

hence $\cos 2A + \sin 2A = -\dfrac{8}{17} + \dfrac{15}{17}$

$$= \dfrac{7}{17} \text{ as given.}$$

3. Circle has general equation $x^2 + y^2 + 2gx + 2fy + c = 0$ with centre $(-g, -f)$ and radius $\sqrt{g^2 + f^2 - c}$.
Given circle has equation $x^2 + y^2 - 8x + 11 = 0$

Hence $2g = -8$ and $2f = 0$

So centre is $(4, 0)$

$c = 11 \qquad$ Radius is $\sqrt{4^2 - 11}$

$$= \sqrt{5}$$

Centre $(4, 0)$ radius $\sqrt{5}$

The circle with radius twice as long has radius $2\sqrt{5}$

The distance between the two centres is $\sqrt{5} + 2\sqrt{5} = 3\sqrt{5}$

Let centre of small circle $= C_1$

Let centre of large circle $= C_2$

Let point of intersection $= P(6, 1)$

$\overrightarrow{C_1P} : \overrightarrow{PC_2}$ has ratio $1 : 2$

$\overrightarrow{C_1P} = p - c_1 = \begin{pmatrix} 6 \\ 1 \end{pmatrix} - \begin{pmatrix} 4 \\ 0 \end{pmatrix} = \begin{pmatrix} 2 \\ 1 \end{pmatrix}$

$\overrightarrow{PC_2} = 2\overrightarrow{C_1P} = 2\begin{pmatrix} 2 \\ 1 \end{pmatrix} = \begin{pmatrix} 4 \\ 2 \end{pmatrix}$

$\overrightarrow{OC_2} = \overrightarrow{OP} + \overrightarrow{PC_2} = \begin{pmatrix} 6 \\ 1 \end{pmatrix} + \begin{pmatrix} 4 \\ 2 \end{pmatrix} = \begin{pmatrix} 10 \\ 3 \end{pmatrix} \qquad C_2 = (10, 3)$

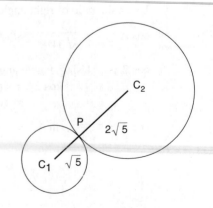

Hence centre of the larger circle $= (10, 3)$
$$\text{radius} = 2\sqrt{5}$$
Equation is
$$(x - 10)^2 + (y - 3)^2 = (2\sqrt{5})^2$$
$$\Leftrightarrow \quad x^2 - 20x + 100 + y^2 - 6y + 9 = 20$$
$$\Leftrightarrow \quad x^2 + y^2 - 20x - 6y + 89 = 0$$

Alternative Method:

By using $-g = 10, -f = 3, c = 2\sqrt{5}$

in the general equation
$$x^2 + y^2 + 2gx + 2fy + c = 0$$
$$\Leftrightarrow \quad x^2 + y^2 + 2(-10)x + 2(-3)y + c = 0$$
$$x^2 + y^2 - 20x - 6y + c = 0$$

and now find c by solving
$$r = 2\sqrt{5}$$
$$r = \sqrt{g^2 + f^2 - c}$$
$$2\sqrt{5} = \sqrt{10^2 + 3^2 - c}$$
$$20 = 109 - c$$
$$\Rightarrow c = 89$$

Hence equation of circle $= x^2 + y^2 - 20x - 6y + 89 = 0$

4.

$$f(x) > 0, -4 < x < 0,$$
$$f'(x) < 0, -2 < x < 2$$

$f(x)$ positive for all points
above the x-axis

$f'(x) = m$, (gradient)
gradient negative between $x = -2$ and
$$x = 2$$

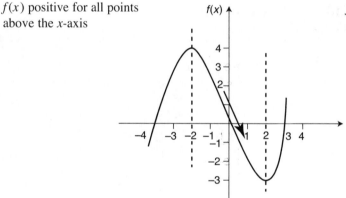

$f(x) > 0$ and $f'(x) < 0$
$$\Rightarrow \{x : -2 < x < 0, x \in R\}$$

5. *(a)*
$$x^2 - 6x + 4 = (x^2 - 6x) + 4$$
$$= (x^2 - 6x + 9) + 4 - 9$$
$$= (x - 3)^2 - 5$$
Since the least value of any square number is 0, then $(x - 3)^2$ has minimum value 0.
Hence the minimum value of the function is -5 when $x = 3$.
Minimum value of the function is $(3 - 3)^2 - 5$ and the
coordinates of the minimum turning point $(3, -5)$.

(b) y-intersection $(0, 4)$, minimum turning point $(3, -5)$.

(c) Since the minimum turning point $(3, -5)$ lies below
the x-axis, the curve crosses the x-axis in two places
and the equation has 2 real distinct roots.

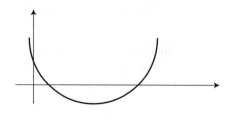

6. (a) $f(x) = x^2 - 3$ and $g(x) = 2x + 1$

$$f(g(x))$$
$$= f(2x + 1)$$
$$= (2x + 1)^2 - 3$$
$$= 4x^2 + 4x + 1 - 3$$
$$= 4x^2 + 4x - 2$$

$$g(f(x))$$
$$= g(x^2 - 3)$$
$$= 2(x^2 - 3) + 1$$
$$2x^2 - 6 + 1 = 2x^2 - 5$$

$$f(g(x)) - g(f(x))$$
$$= 4x^2 + 4x - 2 - (2x^2 - 5)$$
$$= 2x^2 + 4x + 3$$

(b) If $f(g(x)) - g(f(x)) = 9$
then $2x^2 + 4x + 3 = 9$
$2x^2 + 4x - 6 = 0$; $2(x^2 + 2x - 3) = 0$; $2(x + 3)(x - 1) = 0$ $x = -3$ or $x = 1$

Check $f(g(-3))$ $g(-3) = 2(-3) + 1 = -5$; $f(-5) = (-5)^2 - 3 = 22$

$\quad\quad g(f(x)) = g(f(-3))$; $f(x) = x^2 - 3$; $f(-3) = (-3)^2 - 3 = 6$; $g(6) = 2(6) + 1 = 13$

and $22 - 13 = 9$ you could also check with $x = 1$

$$f(g(1)) - g(f(1)) = 2(1)^2 + 4(1) + 3 = 9$$
$$f(g(-3)) - g(f(-3)) = 2(-3)^2 + 4(-3) + 3 = 9$$

7. (a) $u_{n+1} = 2u_n + 3$

$\quad\quad u_{n+2} = 2u_{n+1} + 3$
$\quad\quad\quad\quad = 2(2u_n + 3) + 3$
$\quad\quad u_{n+2} = 4u_n + 9$

(b) $u_{n+1} = 2u_n + 3$
$\quad\quad u_{n+3} = 2u_{n+2} + 3$
$\quad\quad\quad\quad = 2(4u_n + 9) + 3$
$\quad\quad u_{n+3} = 8u_n + 21$
$\quad\quad u_{n+3} = 53$
$\quad\quad 8u_n + 21 = 53$
$\quad\quad 8u_n \quad = 32$
$\quad\quad u_n \quad = 4$

(c) Find u_{n-1}
$$u_n = 2u_{n-1} + 3$$
$$4 = 2u_{n-1} + 3$$
$$2u_{n-1} = 1; \quad u_{n-1} = \frac{1}{2}$$

Find u_{n+4}
$$u_{n+4} = 2u_{n+3} + 3$$
$$= 2(53) + 3$$
$$= 109$$

8. $f(x) = (x^2 - 3x)^3$

Find $f'(x)$ by chain rule method.

$$
\begin{aligned}
f'(x) &= 3(x^2 - 3x)^2(2x - 3) \\
&= 3(2x - 3)(x^2 - 3x)^2 \\
f'(-1) &= 3(2(-1) - 3)((-1)^2 - 3(-1))^2 \\
&= 3(-5)(1 + 3)^2 \\
&= -15(4)^2 \\
&= -240 \\
f'(-1) &= -240
\end{aligned}
$$

9. $\displaystyle\int_a^3 (3x^2 - 2x)\,dx = 20 \Rightarrow \left[\dfrac{3x^{2+1}}{2+1} - \dfrac{2x^{1+1}}{1+1}\right]_a^3 = 20$

$$
\begin{aligned}
&= \left[\dfrac{3x^3}{3} - \dfrac{2x^2}{2}\right]_a^3 = 20 \\
&= [x^3 - x^2]_a^3 = 20
\end{aligned}
$$

$$
\begin{aligned}
\Rightarrow (3^3 - 3^2) - (a^3 - a^2) &= 20 \\
\Rightarrow 18 - a^3 + a^2 &= 20 \\
\Rightarrow a^2 - a^3 &= 2 \\
\Rightarrow a^2(1 - a) &= 2 \\
\Rightarrow 2^2(1 - 2) &\neq 2 \\
(-1)^2(1 - (-1)) & \\
1(2) &= 2 \\
\Rightarrow a &= -1
\end{aligned}
$$

By trial and error
assume that $a < 3$

*By synthetic division using $-a^3 - a^2 = 2$ as $a^3 - a^2 + 2 = 0$

$$
\begin{array}{c|cccc}
 & a^3 & a^2 & a^1 & a^0 \\
-1 & 1 & -1 & 0 & 2 \\
 & & -1 & +2 & -2 \\
\hline
 & 1 & -2 & +2 & 0
\end{array}
$$

Since $a^3 - a^2 + 2$ is divisible by -1 then $(a + 1)$ is a factor

$$\Rightarrow a = -1$$

10.

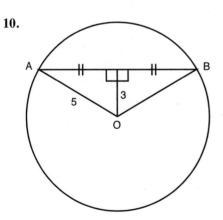

Let mid-point of chord $AB = P$

Using the Theorem of Pythagoras on right-angled triangle $P\hat{O}B$

$$
\begin{aligned}
OB &= \text{radius} = 5, |OP| = 3 \\
PB^2 &= 5^2 - 3^2 \\
PB^2 &= 16 \Rightarrow PB = 4
\end{aligned}
$$

Using ratio of right-angled triangles $\cos P\hat{O}B = \dfrac{3}{5}$

$$\sin P\hat{O}B = \dfrac{4}{5}$$

To find $\sin \stackrel{\wedge}{\text{AOB}}$

$$\stackrel{\wedge}{\text{AOB}} = 2\stackrel{\wedge}{\text{POB}}$$

Let $\stackrel{\wedge}{\text{AOB}} = x$, hence $\stackrel{\wedge}{\text{POB}} = 2x$

$$\sin 2x = 2 \sin x \cos x$$

$$\sin x = \frac{4}{5}, \quad \cos x = \frac{3}{5}$$

$$2 \sin x \cos x$$

$$= 2\left(\frac{4}{5}\right)\left(\frac{3}{5}\right)$$

$$= 2\left(\frac{12}{25}\right)$$

$$= \frac{24}{25}$$

11. (a) A(3, 1, 4), B(6, 7, 10)

$$a = \begin{pmatrix} 3 \\ 1 \\ 4 \end{pmatrix}, \quad b = \begin{pmatrix} 6 \\ 7 \\ 10 \end{pmatrix}$$

$$\overrightarrow{AP} : \overrightarrow{PB}$$

$$1 : 2$$

$$\Rightarrow \quad 2\overrightarrow{AP} = \overrightarrow{PB}$$

$$\overrightarrow{AP} = p - a \qquad\qquad \overrightarrow{PB} = b - p$$

$$\Rightarrow \quad 2\overrightarrow{AP} = 2(p - a) \qquad\qquad \overrightarrow{PB} = (b - p)$$

$$\Rightarrow 2p - 2a = b - p$$

$$3p = 2a + b$$

$$\Rightarrow \quad 3p = 2\begin{pmatrix} 3 \\ 1 \\ 4 \end{pmatrix} + \begin{pmatrix} 6 \\ 7 \\ 10 \end{pmatrix}$$

$$\begin{pmatrix} 6 \\ 2 \\ 8 \end{pmatrix} + \begin{pmatrix} 6 \\ 7 \\ 10 \end{pmatrix} = \begin{pmatrix} 12 \\ 9 \\ 18 \end{pmatrix}$$

$$3p = \begin{pmatrix} 12 \\ 9 \\ 18 \end{pmatrix} \Rightarrow p = \begin{pmatrix} 4 \\ 3 \\ 6 \end{pmatrix}$$

$$p = \overrightarrow{OP} \qquad \text{Hence } P = (4, 3, 6)$$

<u>Alternative Method:</u>

This can also be solved using the section formula.

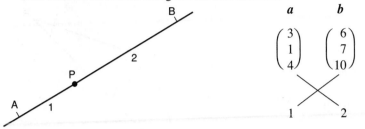

$$P = \frac{1}{3}(2a + b)$$

$$= \frac{1}{3}\left[\begin{pmatrix} 6 \\ 2 \\ 8 \end{pmatrix} + \begin{pmatrix} 6 \\ 7 \\ 10 \end{pmatrix}\right]$$

$$= \frac{1}{3}\begin{pmatrix} 12 \\ 9 \\ 18 \end{pmatrix} = (4, 3, 6)$$

(b) $A(3, 1, 4), P(4, 3, 6), B(6, 7, 10)$

$\Rightarrow \quad \overrightarrow{AP} = \boldsymbol{p} - \boldsymbol{a} \qquad\qquad \overrightarrow{BP} = \boldsymbol{p} - \boldsymbol{b}$

$$\boldsymbol{p} - \boldsymbol{a} = \begin{pmatrix} 4 \\ 3 \\ 6 \end{pmatrix} - \begin{pmatrix} 3 \\ 1 \\ 4 \end{pmatrix} \qquad \boldsymbol{p} - \boldsymbol{b} = \begin{pmatrix} 4 \\ 3 \\ 6 \end{pmatrix} - \begin{pmatrix} 6 \\ 7 \\ 10 \end{pmatrix}$$

$$= \begin{pmatrix} 1 \\ 2 \\ 2 \end{pmatrix} \qquad\qquad\qquad = \begin{pmatrix} -2 \\ -4 \\ -4 \end{pmatrix}$$

$$\overrightarrow{AP} : \overrightarrow{BP} = 1 : -2$$

12. *(a)* Using synthetic division

	x^3	$+$	$6x^2$	$+$	$5x$	$-$	12
$x = -3$	1		6		5		-12
			-3		-9		-12
	1		3		-4		0

Remainder = 0; $f(-3) = 0$

Since the remainder = 0, -3 is a root and $(x + 3)$ is a factor

$$x^3 + 6x^2 + 5x - 12 = (x + 3)(x^2 + 3x - 4)$$

By factorising the second bracket further . . . $f(x) = (x + 3)(x - 1)(x + 4)$

(b) $f(x)$ meets the x-axis when $y = 0$; $(x + 3)(x - 1)(x + 4) = 0$

$(x + 3) = 0$ or $(x - 1) = 0$ or $(x + 4) = 0$

$x = -3, x = 1, x = -4$

Coordinates are $(-3, 0)(1, 0)(-4, 0)$

$f(x)$ meets the y-axis when $x = 0$; $f(0) = -12$; coordinates are $(0, -12)$.

Hence $f(x)$ meets the axes at points $(-4, 0), (-3, 0), (1, 0), (0, -12)$.

WORKED EXAMPLE — TEST PAPER B

1. $P(2, -1), Q(3, 2), R(6, 5)$

   gradient of PR $= \dfrac{5 - (-1)}{6 - 2}$

   $$\dfrac{6}{4} = \dfrac{3}{2} = m$$

   If line QA is perpendicular to line PR

   then $\quad m_{QA} \cdot m_{PR} = -1$

   $m_{PR} = \dfrac{3}{2}$ hence $m_{QA} = -\dfrac{2}{3}$

   Point on QA $= Q(3, 2)$ gradient of QA $= -\dfrac{2}{3}$

   $$y - b = m(x - a)$$

   $$y - 2 = -\dfrac{2}{3}(x - 3)$$

   $$3y - 6 = -2x + 6$$

   $3y + 2x = 12$ is the equation of the altitude QA.

2. $P(2, a, -3), Q(1, a, a)$

   $\overrightarrow{OP} = \boldsymbol{p} = \begin{pmatrix} 2 \\ a \\ -3 \end{pmatrix}, \overrightarrow{OQ} = \boldsymbol{q} = \begin{pmatrix} 1 \\ a \\ a \end{pmatrix}$

   If $\overrightarrow{OP}$ is perpendicular to $\overrightarrow{OQ}$, then $\boldsymbol{p} \cdot \boldsymbol{q} = 0$

   $\Rightarrow \quad \begin{pmatrix} 2 \\ a \\ -3 \end{pmatrix} \cdot \begin{pmatrix} 1 \\ a \\ a \end{pmatrix} = 0$

   $\Rightarrow \quad 2 + a^2 - 3a = 0$

   $\Rightarrow \quad a^2 - 3a + 2 = 0$

   $\quad (a - 1)(a - 2) = 0$

   $\quad a = 2 \quad$ or $\quad a = 1$

   Check with $a = 2$; $\begin{pmatrix} 2 \\ 2 \\ -3 \end{pmatrix} \cdot \begin{pmatrix} 1 \\ 2 \\ 2 \end{pmatrix} = 2 + 4 - 6 = 0$

   Check with $a = 1$; $\begin{pmatrix} 2 \\ 1 \\ -3 \end{pmatrix} \cdot \begin{pmatrix} 1 \\ 1 \\ 1 \end{pmatrix} = 2 + 1 - 3 = 0$

3. (a) $x^2 + y^2 - 4x + 2y + 1 = 0$

   General equation of a circle $x^2 + y^2 + 2gx + 2fy + c = 0$

   where centre $= (-g, -f)$

   $\quad$ radius $= \sqrt{g^2 + f^2 - c}$

   $x^2 + y^2 - 4x + 2y + 1 = 0$

   $2g = -4, 2f = 2$

   $-g = 2, -f = -1, c = 1$

   $\quad$ radius $= \sqrt{2^2 + 1^2 - 1} = \sqrt{4} = 2$

   Hence centre $= (2, -1)$, radius $= 2$

(b) Reflected in the *x*-axis

centre = (2, 1)

radius unchanged

New equation is
$$x^2 + y^2 - 4x - 2y + 1 = 0$$

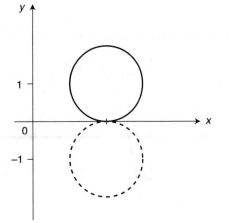

4. $f(x) = x^3 + mx$

$f'(x) = 3x^2 + m$

$3x^2 + m =$ gradient of tangent

gradient $= 0$ for stationary value

$\Rightarrow 3x^2 + m = 0$

$x = \pm 1 \Rightarrow 3(-1)^2 + m = 0$

$\qquad\qquad\qquad 3 + m = 0$

$\Rightarrow \qquad\qquad m = -3$

$f(x) = x^3 - 3x$

5. $(\sqrt{3} + 2\sqrt{2})^2.$

$= (\sqrt{3} + 2\sqrt{2})(\sqrt{3} + 2\sqrt{2})$

$= \sqrt{3}(\sqrt{3} + 2\sqrt{2}) + 2\sqrt{2}(\sqrt{3} + 2\sqrt{2})$

$= 3 + 2\sqrt{6} + 2\sqrt{6} + 8$

$= 11 + 4\sqrt{6}$

6.

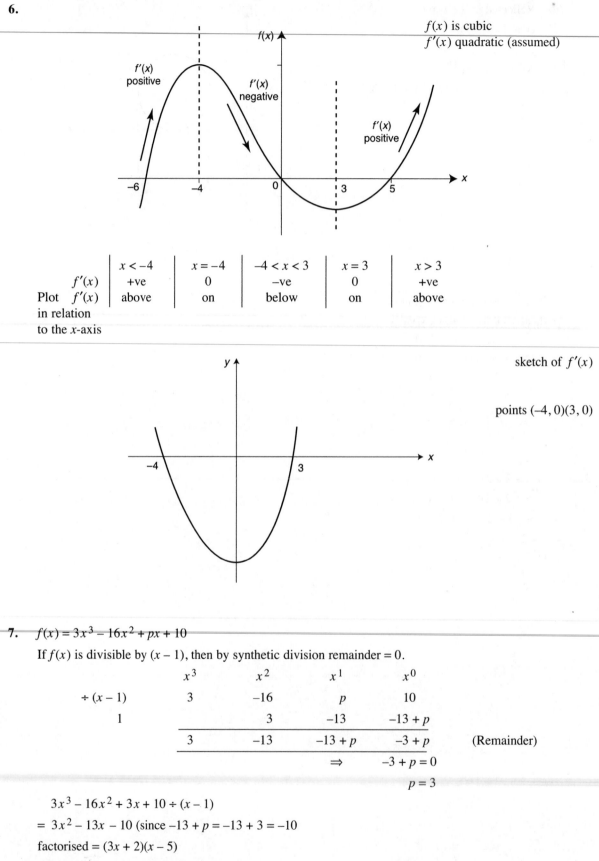

$f(x)$ is cubic
$f'(x)$ quadratic (assumed)

	$x < -4$	$x = -4$	$-4 < x < 3$	$x = 3$	$x > 3$
$f'(x)$	+ve	0	−ve	0	+ve
Plot $f'(x)$	above	on	below	on	above

Plot $f'(x)$ in relation to the x-axis

sketch of $f'(x)$

points $(-4, 0)(3, 0)$

7. $f(x) = 3x^3 - 16x^2 + px + 10$

If $f(x)$ is divisible by $(x - 1)$, then by synthetic division remainder $= 0$.

	x^3	x^2	x^1	x^0
$\div (x - 1)$	3	−16	p	10
1		3	−13	$-13 + p$
	3	−13	$-13 + p$	$-3 + p$

(Remainder)

$$\Rightarrow \quad -3 + p = 0$$
$$p = 3$$

$3x^3 - 16x^2 + 3x + 10 \div (x - 1)$

$= 3x^2 - 13x - 10$ (since $-13 + p = -13 + 3 = -10$

factorised $= (3x + 2)(x - 5)$

fully factorised $f(x) = (x - 1)(x - 5)(3x + 2)$

38

8. $f'(x) = 3x - 2$

$f(x) = \dfrac{3x^2}{2} - 2x + c$

$f(2) = \dfrac{3(2)^2}{2} - 2(2) + c$

$\quad\;\; = 6 - 4 + c$

$\quad\;\; = \quad 2 + c$

given $f(2) = 7$

$\Rightarrow \quad 2 + c = 7$

$\Rightarrow \quad\quad\; c = 5$

Hence $f(x) = \dfrac{3x^2}{2} - 2x + 5$

9. $\quad\quad f(x) = 2x^2$

$\quad\quad\; g(x) = 3x - 1$

$f(g(x)) = f(3x - 1)$

$\quad\quad\;\; = 2(3x - 1)^2$

$\quad\quad\;\; = 2(9x^2 - 6x + 1)$

$f(g(x)) = 18x^2 - 12x + 2$

10. *(a)* $\quad 3x^2 - 4x + 2$

$\quad\quad a = 3, b = -4, c = 2$

$\quad\quad b^2 - 4ac < 0$ for no real roots

$\quad\quad (-4)^2 - 4(3)(2)$

$\quad\quad 16 - 24 = -8$

$\quad\quad$ since $\quad -8 \in R$

$\quad\quad$ function has no real roots.

(b) $\quad 3x^2 - 4x + 2$

$\quad\quad 3\left(x^2 - \dfrac{4}{3}x + \dfrac{2}{3}\right)$

$\quad\quad 3\left[\left(x - \dfrac{2}{3}\right)^2 - \dfrac{4}{9} + \dfrac{2}{3}\right]$

$\quad\quad 3\left[\left(x - \dfrac{2}{3}\right)^2 + \dfrac{2}{9}\right]$

$\quad = 3\left(x - \dfrac{2}{3}\right)^2 + \dfrac{2}{3}$

$\quad\quad$ minimum value $= \dfrac{2}{3}$ when $x = \dfrac{2}{3}$

$\quad\quad$ minimum turning point $= \left(\dfrac{2}{3}, \dfrac{2}{3}\right)$

$\quad\quad$ cuts y-axis at $(0, 2)$

(c)   Sketch of $f(x)$

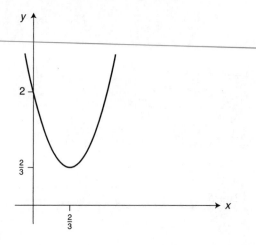

11. (a) $u_{r+1} = mu_r + c$, $u_0 = 1$, $u_1 = -3$, $u_2 = 21$

$u_1 = mu_0 + c \Rightarrow -3 = m(1) + c$ ①

$u_2 = mu_1 + c \Rightarrow 21 = m(-3) + c$ ②

① − ② − 24 = 4m, ⇒ m = −6

Substitute $m = -6$ in ①

$-3 = -6(1) + c$

$3 = c$ $u_2 = -6u_1 + 3$

$m = -6$ $c = 3$ check $-6(-3) + 3$

$u_{r+1} = -6u_r + 3$ $= 18 + 3 = 21$

(b) $u_3 = -6u_2 + c$

$= -6(21) + 3$

$= -126 + 3 = -123$

$u_3 = -123$

To find u_{-1} use $u_0 = -6u_{-1} + 3$

$u_0 = 1 \Rightarrow 1 = -6u_{-1} + 3$

$\Rightarrow -2 = -6u_{-1}$

$\Rightarrow \dfrac{1}{3} = u_{-1}$

(c)   To find $u_r = u_{r+1}$

$u_{r+1} = -6u_r + 3$

$\Rightarrow u_r = -6u_r + 3$

$\Rightarrow 7u_r = 3$

$\Rightarrow u_r = \dfrac{3}{7}$

Check $u_r = \dfrac{3}{7}$, $u_{r+1} = -6\left(\dfrac{3}{7}\right) + 3$

$= \dfrac{-18}{7} + 3$

$= \dfrac{-18}{7} + \dfrac{21}{7} = \dfrac{3}{7}$

Gives (u_r, u_{r+1}), $\left(\dfrac{3}{7}, \dfrac{3}{7}\right)$, $u_r = u_{r+1}$

12. Using Pythagoras' Theorem, third side is $\sqrt{21}$

$\sin x = \dfrac{2}{5}$ $\cos x = \dfrac{\sqrt{21}}{5}$

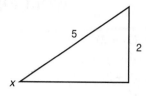

$\sin 2x = 2 \sin x \cos x = 2 \left(\dfrac{2}{5}\right) \cdot \left(\dfrac{\sqrt{21}}{5}\right) = \left(\dfrac{4\sqrt{21}}{25}\right)$

$\cos 2x = \cos^2 x - \sin^2 x = \left(\dfrac{\sqrt{21}}{5}\right)^2 - \left(\dfrac{2}{5}\right)^2$

$\dfrac{21}{25} - \dfrac{4}{25} = \dfrac{17}{25}$

1.

$y = 5\log_2(2x + 2)$
At B, $x = 0$
$y = 5\log_2(0 + 2)$
$y = 5\log_2(2)$
$y = 5 \times 1 = 5$
coordinates of B(0, 5)

$y = 5\log_2(2x + 2)$
At C, $y = 10$
$\quad = 5\log_2(2x + 2) = 10$
$\log_2(2x + 2) = 2$
$2^2 = 2x + 2$
$2x + 2 = 4$
$2x = 2; x = 1$

coordinates of C(1, 10)

$y = 5\log_2(2x + 2)$
At A, $y = 0$
$5\log_2(2x + 2) = 0$
$\log_2(2x + 2)^5 = 0$
$2^0 = (2x + 2)^5$
$(2x + 2)^5 = 1$
$2x + 2 = 1$
$2x = -1; x = -\dfrac{1}{2}$

coordinates of A $\left(-\dfrac{1}{2}, 0\right)$

2.

$f(x) = 2x^3 + mx$
$f'(x) = 6x^2 + m$ (the gradient of the tangent)
$f'(2) = 6(2)^2 + m$ (Note $f'(-2) = f'(2)$)
The gradient of the tangent = 0 for stationary values.
Hence $\quad f'(2) = 0$
$\Rightarrow 24 + m = 0$
$\qquad m = -24$
So $\qquad f(x) = 2x^3 - 24x$
and $\qquad f(-1) = 2(-1)^3 - 24(-1)$
$\qquad\qquad = -2 + 24$
$\qquad\qquad = 22$

3. *(a)* Circle $x^2 + y^2 - 2x + 6y + 1 = 0$

General equation of a circle is $x^2 + y^2 + 2gx + 2fy + c = 0$

where centre $= (-g, -f)$ and radius $= \sqrt{g^2 + f^2 - c}$

hence centre $= (1, -3)$, radius $= \sqrt{1^2 + 3^2 - 1} = 3$

(b) Centre $(1, -3)$ reflected in y-axis $= (-1, -3)$

$-g = -1$, hence $2g = 2$, f unchanged, r unchanged.

Equation of circle after reflection in the y-axis is

$\qquad x^2 + y^2 + 2x + 6y + 1 = 0$

4. $A(-1, 3), B(2, -1), C(5, 4)$

$m_{AC} \dfrac{4-3}{5-(-1)} = \dfrac{1}{6}$ (the gradient of line AC)

If AC is perpendicular to BQ

then $m_{AC} \times m_{BQ} = -1$

$m_{AC} = \dfrac{1}{6}$ hence $m_{BQ} = -6$

$m_{BQ} = -6$ through $B(2, -1)$

$$y - b = m(x - a)$$
$$y + 1 = -6(x - 2)$$
$$y + 1 = -6x + 12$$
$$y = -6x + 11$$

Equation of BQ is $y + 6x = 11$

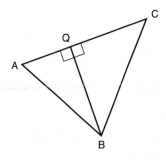

5. Graph of $f(x)$.

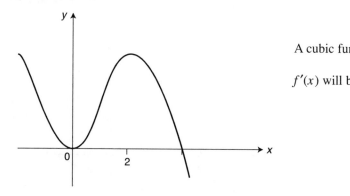

A cubic function $ax^3 + bx + c$

$f'(x)$ will be of form $3ax^2 + b$ which is a quadratic

x	$x < 0$	$x = 0$	$0 < x < 2$	$x = 2$	$x > 2$
$f'(x)$	$-$ve	0	$+$ve	0	$-$ve
Plot $f'(x)$ in relation to the x-axis	below	on	above	on	below

x	$x < 0$	$x = 0$	$0 < x < 2$	$x = 2$	$x > 2$
Plotting points in $\Rightarrow$ relation to x-axis	below	on	above	on	below
Plot		$(0, 0)$		$(2, 0)$	

Graph of $f'(x)$

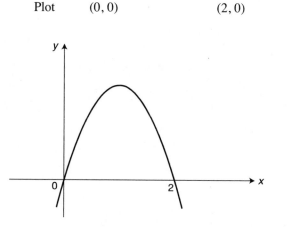

43

6. (*a*) Using synthetic division

$$x^3 + 3x^2 - 13x - 15$$

$$
\begin{array}{r|rrrr}
x = -1 & 1 & 3 & -13 & -15 \\
       &   & -1 & -2 & 15 \\
\hline
       & 1 & 2 & -15 & 0
\end{array}
$$
Remainder $= 0$; $f(-1) = 0$

Since the remainder $= 0$, -1 is a root and $(x + 1)$ is a factor

$$x^3 + 3x^2 - 13x - 15 = (x + 1)(x^2 + 2x - 15)$$

By factorising the second bracket further . . . $f(x) = (x + 1)(x - 3)(x + 5)$

(*b*) $f(x)$ meets the x-axis when $y = 0$; $(x + 1)(x - 3)(x + 5) = 0$
$(x + 1) = 0$ or $(x - 3) = 0$ or $(x + 5) = 0$
$x = -1, x = 3, x = -5$
coordinates are $(-1, 0)(3, 0)(-5, 0)$

$f(x)$ meets the y-axis when $x = 0$; $f(0) = -15$; coordinate is $(0, -15)$

Hence $f(x)$ meets the axes at the points $(-5, 0), (-1, 0), (3, 0), (0, -15)$

7. (*a*) A $(2, -1, 3)$, B $(1, 6, -4)$
P divides AB in the ratio $2 : -3$

$$a = \begin{pmatrix} 2 \\ -1 \\ 3 \end{pmatrix}, \quad b = \begin{pmatrix} 1 \\ 6 \\ -4 \end{pmatrix}$$

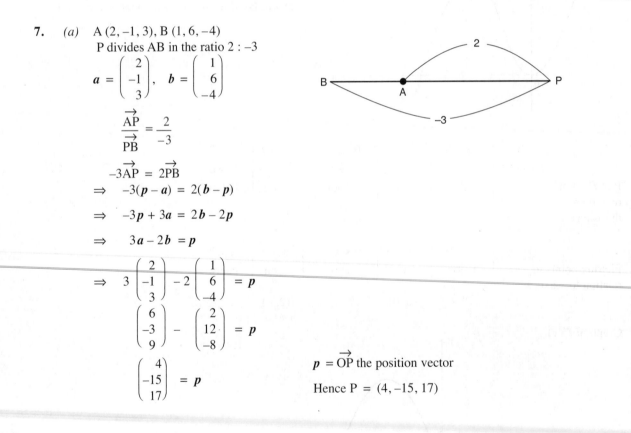

$$\frac{\overrightarrow{AP}}{\overrightarrow{PB}} = \frac{2}{-3}$$

$$-3\overrightarrow{AP} = 2\overrightarrow{PB}$$

$$\Rightarrow \quad -3(p - a) = 2(b - p)$$

$$\Rightarrow \quad -3p + 3a = 2b - 2p$$

$$\Rightarrow \quad 3a - 2b = p$$

$$\Rightarrow \quad 3\begin{pmatrix} 2 \\ -1 \\ 3 \end{pmatrix} - 2\begin{pmatrix} 1 \\ 6 \\ -4 \end{pmatrix} = p$$

$$\begin{pmatrix} 6 \\ -3 \\ 9 \end{pmatrix} - \begin{pmatrix} 2 \\ 12 \\ -8 \end{pmatrix} = p$$

$$\begin{pmatrix} 4 \\ -15 \\ 17 \end{pmatrix} = p$$

$p = \overrightarrow{OP}$ the position vector

Hence P $= (4, -15, 17)$

44

Alternative Method:

This can also be done by section formula.

A(2, -1, 3)   B(1, 6, -4)

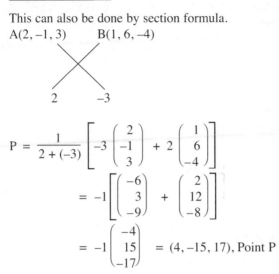

2   -3

$$P = \frac{1}{2 + (-3)}\left[-3\begin{pmatrix} 2 \\ -1 \\ 3 \end{pmatrix} + 2\begin{pmatrix} 1 \\ 6 \\ -4 \end{pmatrix}\right]$$

$$= -1\left[\begin{pmatrix} -6 \\ 3 \\ -9 \end{pmatrix} + \begin{pmatrix} 2 \\ 12 \\ -8 \end{pmatrix}\right]$$

$$= -1\begin{pmatrix} -4 \\ 15 \\ -17 \end{pmatrix} = (4, -15, 17), \text{ Point P}$$

(b) $\overrightarrow{AB} : \overrightarrow{PB}$

$$\overrightarrow{AB} = b - a = \begin{pmatrix} 1 \\ 6 \\ -4 \end{pmatrix} - \begin{pmatrix} 2 \\ -1 \\ 3 \end{pmatrix} = \begin{pmatrix} -1 \\ 7 \\ -7 \end{pmatrix}$$

$$\overrightarrow{PB} = b - p = \begin{pmatrix} 1 \\ 6 \\ -4 \end{pmatrix} - \begin{pmatrix} 4 \\ -15 \\ 17 \end{pmatrix} = \begin{pmatrix} -3 \\ 21 \\ -21 \end{pmatrix} = \overrightarrow{PB}, \text{ hence } \overrightarrow{BP} = \begin{pmatrix} 3 \\ -21 \\ 21 \end{pmatrix}$$

$\overrightarrow{AP} : \overrightarrow{PB} = 1 : 3$ and $\overrightarrow{AB} : \overrightarrow{BP} = -1 : 3$

8. *(a)* $x^2 + 4x + 11 = (x^2 + 4x) + 11$
$$= (x^2 + 4x + 4) + 11 - 4$$
$$= (x + 2)^2 + 7$$

Since the least value of any square number is 0 then $(x + 2)^2$ has minimum value 0.
Hence the minimum value of the function is $0 + 7$ when $x = -2$
Minimum value of the function is $(-2 + 2)^2 + 7$
and the coordinates of the minimum turning point $(-2, 7)$.

(b) *y*-intersection $(0, 11)$, minimum turning point $(-2, 7)$.

(c) Since the minimum turning point $(-2, 7)$ lies above the *x*-axis, the curve does not cross the *x*-axis, the equation has no real roots.

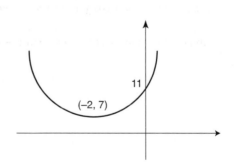

9. $u_{n+1} = 0\cdot4u_n + 12$;

$u_{n+1} = au_n + 12$, a limit exists when $-1 < a < 1$

~~a is a fraction lying between -1 and 1~~

Let $L = u_n$; $L = 0\cdot4L + 12$

$0\cdot6L = 12$

$L = 12 \div 0\cdot6$

$L = 20$

Check with $u_n = 20$; $u_{n+1} = 0\cdot4u_n + 12$

$u_{n+1} = 0\cdot4(20) + 12$; $u_{n+1} = 20$

input = output

10. $(1, 2), (a, 4), (b, 1)$

Let points = A, B, C respectively.

If points are collinear, then they have equal gradients,

i.e., $m_{AB} = m_{BC}$, B lies on line AC

$m_{AB} = \dfrac{4-2}{a-1}$, $m_{BC} = \dfrac{1-4}{b-a}$

$\Rightarrow \quad m_{AB} = \dfrac{2}{a-1}$, $m_{BC} = \dfrac{-3}{b-a}$

$\Rightarrow \quad \dfrac{2}{a-1} = \dfrac{-3}{b-a}$

$\Rightarrow \quad 2(b-a) = -3(a-1)$

$\Rightarrow \quad 2(b-a) = -3a + 3$

$\Rightarrow \quad a + 2b = 3$

11. $\tan x = \dfrac{5}{12}$; $\tan y = \dfrac{3}{4}$

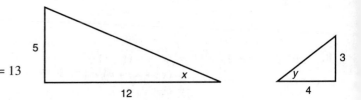

Angle x

opp = 5, adj = 12 giving hypotenuse = 13

$\sin x = \dfrac{5}{13}$; $\cos x = \dfrac{12}{13}$

Angle y

opp = 3, adj = 4 giving hypotenuse = 5

$\sin y = \dfrac{3}{5}$; $\cos y = \dfrac{4}{5}$

$\cos(x-y) = \cos x \cos y + \sin x \sin y \rightarrow \dfrac{12}{13} \cdot \dfrac{4}{5} + \dfrac{5}{13} \cdot \dfrac{3}{5} \rightarrow = \dfrac{63}{65}$

$\sin(x+y) = \sin x \cos y + \cos x \sin y \rightarrow \dfrac{5}{13} \cdot \dfrac{4}{5} + \dfrac{12}{13} \cdot \dfrac{3}{5} \rightarrow = \dfrac{56}{65}$

$\dfrac{63}{65} - \dfrac{56}{65} = \dfrac{7}{65}$

12. $\int_{b}^{2}(3x^2 - 2)\,dx = 3 \Rightarrow [x^3 - 2x]_{b}^{2} = 3$

$$(2^3 - 2(2)) - (b^3 - 2(b)) = 3$$
$$(8 - 4) - b^3 + 2b = 3$$
$$4 - b^3 + 2b = 3$$
$$1 = b^3 - 2b$$
$$1 = b(b^2 - 2)$$
$$b = -1$$

*   Since $b < 2$ Trial and error

Try, $b = 1, 0$ or -1

$-1((-1)^2 - 2)$

$= -1(1 - 2) = -1(-1) = 1$

1. By Pythagoras' Theorem

$$AC^2 = 3^2 + 2^2 = 13$$

$$\cos A = \frac{2}{\sqrt{13}}$$

rationalise denominator $\quad \dfrac{2}{\sqrt{13}} \times \dfrac{\sqrt{13}}{\sqrt{13}} = \dfrac{2\sqrt{13}}{13}$

$$\cos A = \frac{2\sqrt{13}}{13} = \frac{2}{13}\sqrt{13}$$

In form $p\sqrt{13} \Rightarrow p = \dfrac{2}{13}$

2. $f(x) = \sin^3 x + \cos^2 x$

$\sin^3 x = (\sin x)^3$

By chain rule method if $f(x) = (\sin x)^3$

$$\text{then } f'(x) = 3(\sin x)^2 \cos x$$
$$= 3 \cos x \sin^2 x$$

and $\cos^2 x = (\cos x)^2$

By chain rule method if $f(x) = (\cos x)^2$

$$\text{then } f'(x) = 2(\cos x)^1 (-\sin x)$$
$$= -2 \cos x \sin x$$

Hence $f(x) \qquad = \sin^3 x + \cos^2 x$

$\Rightarrow f'(x) \qquad = 3 \cos x \sin^2 x - 2 \cos x \sin x$

Which factorised $\quad = \sin x \cos x\,(3 \sin x - 2)$

$$f'\!\left(\frac{\pi}{4}\right) = \sin \frac{\pi}{4} \cos \frac{\pi}{4} \left(3 \sin \frac{\pi}{4} - 2\right) \qquad \text{Note: } \sin \frac{\pi}{4} = \cos \frac{\pi}{4} = \frac{1}{\sqrt{2}}$$

$$= \frac{1}{\sqrt{2}} \cdot \frac{1}{\sqrt{2}} \left(\frac{3}{\sqrt{2}} - 2\right)$$

$$= \frac{1}{2}\left(\frac{3}{\sqrt{2}} - 2\right)$$

$$= \frac{3}{2\sqrt{2}} - 1 \quad \text{or} \quad \frac{3 - 2\sqrt{2}}{2\sqrt{2}}$$

3.   Graph of $-f(x)$ Graph of $f(x) + 1$

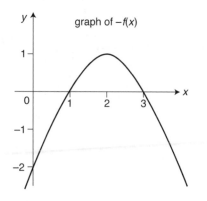

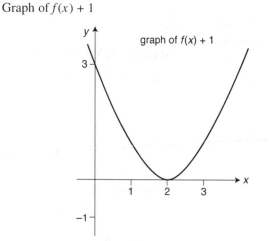

4.   *(a)* $0 \leq x \leq 360$

$f : x \rightarrow \sin 4x$ cuts x-axis when $\sin 4x = 0$

$period = \dfrac{360}{4} = 90$ $4x = 0, 180$

repeats 4 times in $360°$ $x = 0, 45°$

$0, 90 + 0, 180 + 0, 270 + 0, 45, 90 + 45, 180 + 45, 270 + 45$

$x = \{0, 45, 90, 135, 180, 225, 270, 315, 360\}$ 9 times

(b)

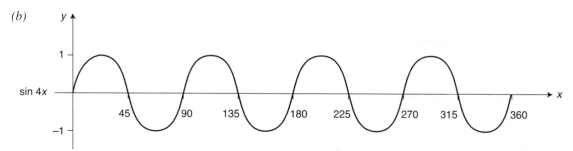

5.   *(a)*   Line which makes an angle of $45°$ with the positive direction of the x-axis has a tangent of 1.

Hence $m = 1$

Line with gradient $= 1$

Passes through point $(0, -1)$

$y - b = m(x - a)$

$y - (-1) = 1(x - 0)$

$y + 1 = x$ or $y = x - 1$ is required equation.

(b)   If a line is perpendicular to another line then the product of their gradients $= -1$.

Hence perpendicular line has gradient $= -1$

Since $1 \times (-1) = -1$

Line with gradient -1 passes through point $(1, 3)$.

$y - b = m(x - a)$

$y - 3 = -1(x - 1)$

$y - 3 = -x + 1$

$y + x = 4$

(c)   Perpendicular line has y-intercept $(0, 4)$ and since $m = -1$ angle made is $135°$.

49

6. *(a)* $A = 3 \cos \left(x - \dfrac{\pi}{6} \right)$

Maximum value $= 3$

when $\left(x - \dfrac{\pi}{6} \right) = 0$

since $\cos 0 = 1$

$\Rightarrow \quad x - \dfrac{\pi}{6} = 0$

$\Rightarrow x = \dfrac{\pi}{6}$

Minimum value $= -3$

when $x - \dfrac{\pi}{6} = \pi$

since $\cos \pi = -1$

$\Rightarrow \quad x - \dfrac{\pi}{6} = \pi$

$x = \pi + \dfrac{\pi}{6}$

$= \dfrac{7\pi}{6}$

Maximum value $= 3$, minimum value $= -3$.

(b) Maximum turning point $\left(\dfrac{\pi}{6}, 3 \right)$

Minimum turning point $\left(\dfrac{7\pi}{6}, -3 \right)$

7. A(1, 2), B(–3, 4), C(5, 6)

$a = \begin{pmatrix} 1 \\ 2 \end{pmatrix} \quad b = \begin{pmatrix} -3 \\ 4 \end{pmatrix} \quad c = \begin{pmatrix} 5 \\ 6 \end{pmatrix}$

We find the position vector of the centroid by:

centroid $= \dfrac{1}{3} (a + b + c)$

$= \dfrac{1}{3} \left[\begin{pmatrix} 1 \\ 2 \end{pmatrix} + \begin{pmatrix} -3 \\ 4 \end{pmatrix} + \begin{pmatrix} 5 \\ 6 \end{pmatrix} \right]$

$= \dfrac{1}{3} \begin{pmatrix} 3 \\ 12 \end{pmatrix} = \begin{pmatrix} 1 \\ 4 \end{pmatrix}$ = position vector

Hence coordinates of centroid $= (1, 4)$

8. P(2, –1, 3)

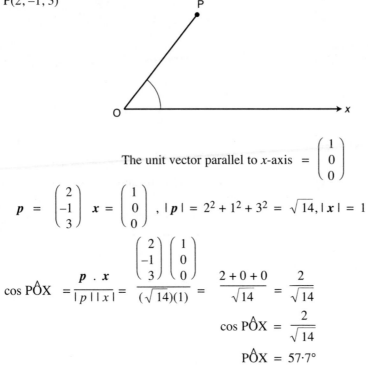

The unit vector parallel to x-axis $= \begin{pmatrix} 1 \\ 0 \\ 0 \end{pmatrix}$

$$p = \begin{pmatrix} 2 \\ -1 \\ 3 \end{pmatrix} \quad x = \begin{pmatrix} 1 \\ 0 \\ 0 \end{pmatrix}, \ |p| = 2^2 + 1^2 + 3^2 = \sqrt{14}, |x| = 1$$

$$\cos P\hat{O}X = \frac{p \cdot x}{|p||x|} = \frac{\begin{pmatrix} 2 \\ -1 \\ 3 \end{pmatrix}\begin{pmatrix} 1 \\ 0 \\ 0 \end{pmatrix}}{(\sqrt{14})(1)} = \frac{2+0+0}{\sqrt{14}} = \frac{2}{\sqrt{14}}$$

$$\cos P\hat{O}X = \frac{2}{\sqrt{14}}$$

$$P\hat{O}X = 57\cdot7°$$

9. $u_{r+1} = mu_r + c, \qquad u_0 = -1, u_1 = 7$ and $u_2 = -9$.

(a) $\quad u_1 \ = m(u_0) + c \Rightarrow \ 7 \ = m(-1) + c$ ①
$\quad\quad u_2 \ = m(u_1) + c \Rightarrow -9 \ = m(7) + c$ ②
$\quad\quad\quad\quad\quad$ ② – ① $- 16 \ = 8m \Rightarrow m = -2$
Substitute $m = -2$ in ① $7 \ = -2(-1) + c$
$\quad\quad\quad\quad\quad\quad\quad\quad 7 \ = 2 + c \Rightarrow c = 5$
Recurrence relation is $u_{r+1} = -2u_r + 5$

(b) $\quad u_3 = -2u_2 + 5$
$\quad\quad\quad = -2(-9) + 5$
$\quad u_3 = 23$

u_{-1} is found by using u_0
$u_0 \ = -2u_{-1} + 5$
$-1 \ = -2u_{-1} + 5$
$-6 \ = -2u_{-1}$
$\dfrac{-6}{-2} \ = u_{-1}$
$3 \ = u_{-1}$
$u_{-1} = 3$

(c) $\quad\quad u_r = u_{r+1}$
$\Rightarrow \ u_r = -2u_r + 5$
$\Rightarrow 3u_r = 5$
$\quad\quad u_r = \dfrac{5}{3}$
Test $-2\left(\dfrac{5}{3}\right) + 5 = \dfrac{5}{3}$

10. $g(x) = 3 - x^2$

$f(x) = 1 - 2x$

$$g(f(x)) = g(1 - 2x) = 3 - (1 - 2x)^2$$
$$= 3 - (1 + 4x^2 - 4x)$$
$$= 3 - 1 - 4x^2 + 4x$$
$$= 2 + 4x - 4x^2$$
$$g(f(x)) = 2(1 + 2x - 2x^2)$$

11. *(a)* $f(x) = 3x^2 - 2x + 5$

$a = 3, b = -2, c = 5$

$b^2 - 4ac$

$(-2)^2 - 4(3)(5)$

$4 - 60 = -56$

$\sqrt{-56} \in R$ $f(x)$ has no real roots.

using the discriminant $b^2 - 4ac$

If $b^2 - 4ac < 0$

$f(x)$ has no real roots.

(b) Completing the square

$3x^2 - 2x + 5$

$$= 3\left(x^2 - \frac{2}{3}x + \frac{5}{3}\right)$$
$$= 3\left[\left(x - \frac{2}{6}\right)^2 - \left(\frac{2}{6}\right)^2 + \frac{5}{3}\right]$$
$$= 3\left[\left(x - \frac{1}{3}\right)^2 - \frac{1}{9} + \frac{5}{3}\right]$$
$$= 3\left[\left(x - \frac{1}{3}\right)^2 + \frac{14}{9}\right]$$
$$= 3\left(x - \frac{1}{3}\right)^2 + \frac{14}{3}$$

$\Rightarrow$ minimum value $= \frac{14}{3}$ when $x = \frac{1}{3}$

Since $\left(x - \frac{1}{3}\right)^2$ is never negative.

Sketch of $3x^2 - 2x + 5$ cuts y-axis at $(0, 5)$.

Minimum T.P. $\left(\frac{1}{3}, \frac{14}{3}\right)$.

(c) Sketch of $f(x)$

sketch of $f(x)$

$\left(\frac{1}{3}, \frac{14}{3}\right)$

12. *(a)* $y = x^3 + 2x^2 - 4$

The point of contact is $(-1, f(-1)) = (-1, -3)$

$f(x) = x^3 + 2x^2 - 4;$ Gradient $= f'(x) = 3x^2 + 4x;$ $m = -1$

Gradient $= f'(-1) = 3(-1)^2 + 4(-1);$ $m = -1$

$m = -1$ through $(-1, -3);$ $y - b = m(x - a)$

$$y - (-3) = -1(x - (-1))$$
$$y + 3 = -x - 1$$
$$y + x = -4 \text{ is the required equation.}$$

(b) $y = -x - 4;$ $m = -1;$ the tangent of the angle $= -1$

$\tan^{-1}(1) = 45°$ in quadrant 1

Since $m = -1$, the angle is in quadrant 2 and

is $180° - 45° = 135°$ (see diagram)

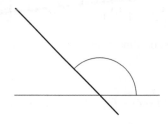

1. AB : BC

2 : 3   hence $3AB = 2BC$

$$3(b - a) = 2(c - b)$$
$$3b - 3a = 2c - 2b$$
$$5b = 3a + 2c$$

$$3\begin{bmatrix} 4 \\ -1 \\ 5 \end{bmatrix} + 2\begin{bmatrix} -1 \\ 4 \\ 10 \end{bmatrix} = \begin{bmatrix} 12 - 2 \\ -3 + 8 \\ 15 + 20 \end{bmatrix} = \begin{bmatrix} 10 \\ 5 \\ 35 \end{bmatrix} = 5b \qquad\qquad b = \begin{bmatrix} 2 \\ 1 \\ 7 \end{bmatrix}$$

The coordinates of $B = (2, 1, 7)$

2. $\displaystyle\int_a^0 (f_1(x) - f_2(x))\,dx + \int_0^b (f_2(x) - f_1(x))\,dx = (\text{upper} - \text{lower})$

$x < 0$ line is upper, $x > 0$ curve is upper,

line $= f_1(x)$ curve $= f_2(x)$

3. $f : x \to \sin 3x$ $0 \le x < 360$

period $= \dfrac{360}{3} = 120$

curve repeats 3 times
in interval 0 to 360.

cuts x-axis when $\sin 3x = 0$

$\Rightarrow 3x = 0, 180, 360, 540$, etc.

$x = \{0, 60, 120, 180, 240, 300\}$

$\sin 3x$ meets the x-axis 6 times.

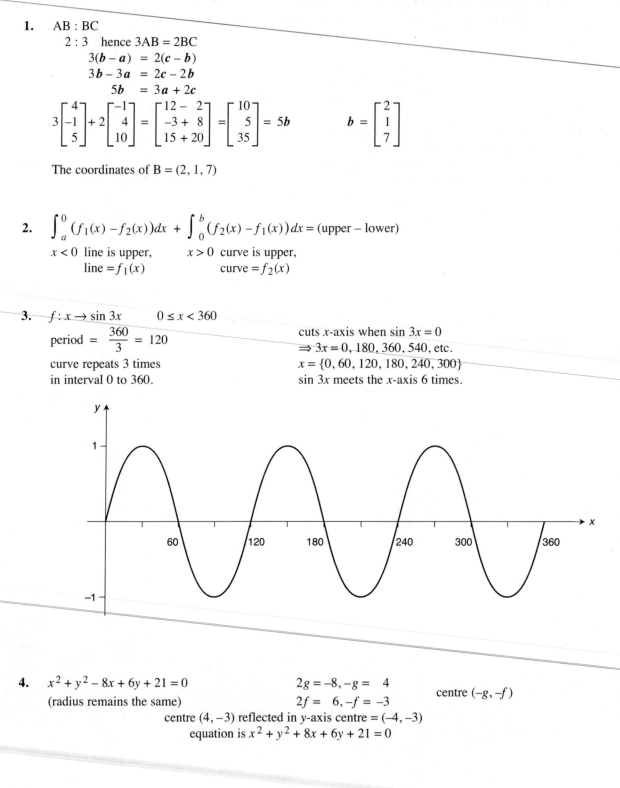

4. $x^2 + y^2 - 8x + 6y + 21 = 0$ $2g = -8, -g = 4$ centre $(-g, -f)$

(radius remains the same) $2f = 6, -f = -3$

centre $(4, -3)$ reflected in y-axis centre $= (-4, -3)$

equation is $x^2 + y^2 + 8x + 6y + 21 = 0$

5. *(a)*
$$1 + 2x - x^2 = -x^2 + 2x + 1 = -1(x^2 - 2x - 1) = -1[(x^2 - 2x + 1) - 1 - 1]$$
$$= -1[(x - 1)^2 - 2]$$
$$= -1(x - 1)^2 + 2$$
$$= 2 - (x - 1)^2$$

Since the least value of any square number is 0,
then $(x - 1)^2$ has minimum value 0.
Hence the maximum value of the function is $2 - 0$
when $x = 1$.
Maximum value of the function is $2 - (1 - 1)^2$
and the coordinates of the maximum turning point $(1, 2)$.

(b) y-intersection $(0, 1)$, maximum turning point $(1, 2)$.

(c) Since the maximum turning point $(1, 2)$ lies above the x-axis, the curve crosses the x-axis in two places and the equation has 2 real roots.

6. $f(x) = 2 \sin 3x,$
$f'(x) = 6 \cos 3x,$
$$f'\left(\frac{\pi}{4}\right) = 6 \cos 3\left(\frac{\pi}{4}\right)$$
$$= 6 \times \frac{-1}{\sqrt{2}} = \frac{-6}{\sqrt{2}} = -3\sqrt{2}$$

7. *(a)* $P(1, 2), Q(6, 3), R(5, -2)$

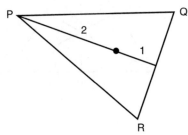

Let mid-point of $QR = L$
$$L = \left(\frac{6 + 5}{2}, \frac{3 - 2}{2}\right)$$
$$L = \left(\frac{11}{2}, \frac{1}{2}\right)$$

Let C = centroid

PC : CL = 2 : 1

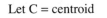

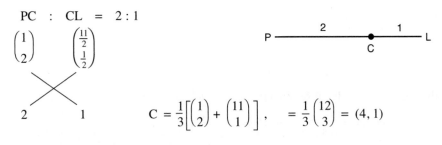

$$C = \frac{1}{3}\left[\binom{1}{2} + \binom{11}{1}\right], \quad = \frac{1}{3}\binom{12}{3} = (4, 1)$$

Alternative Method

$$\overrightarrow{OC} = \frac{1}{3}(p + q + r) = \left(\frac{1 + 6 + 5}{2} \quad \frac{2 + 3 + (-2)}{3}\right) = (4, 1) = C$$

(b) P(1, 2), Q(6, 3), R(5, −2)

$$M = \tfrac{1}{2}(p + r) = \tfrac{1}{2}\binom{6}{0} = (3, 0)$$

$$N = \tfrac{1}{2}(q + p) = \tfrac{1}{2}\binom{7}{5} = \left(\tfrac{7}{2}, \tfrac{5}{2}\right)$$

$$\overrightarrow{QC} = c - q \quad c\binom{4}{1} , \ q\binom{6}{3}$$

$$= \binom{-2}{-2}$$

$$\overrightarrow{QM} = m - q, \ m\binom{3}{0} , \ q\binom{6}{3}$$

$$= \binom{-3}{-3}$$

$$\overrightarrow{QC} : \overrightarrow{QM}$$
$$= 2 : 3$$

$$\overrightarrow{RC} = c - r, \ c\binom{4}{1} , \ r\binom{5}{-2} \qquad \overrightarrow{CN} = n - c, \ n = \binom{\tfrac{7}{2}}{\tfrac{5}{2}}, \quad c = \binom{4}{1}$$

$$c - r = \binom{4 - 5}{1 - (-2)} \qquad\qquad n - c = \binom{\tfrac{7}{2} - \tfrac{8}{2}}{\tfrac{5}{2} - \tfrac{2}{2}}$$

$$= \binom{-1}{3}, \qquad\qquad\qquad = \binom{-\tfrac{1}{2}}{\tfrac{3}{2}}$$

Ratio $\overrightarrow{RC} : \overrightarrow{CN} = 2 : 1$

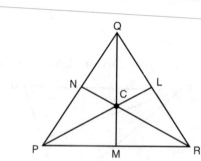

8. $f(x) = x^3 - 3x^2 - 4x + 12$

Try factors of −12
$\{\pm 1, \pm 2, \pm 3, \pm 4, \pm 6\}$
If $f(x) \div (x + 2)$ has remainder zero then $(x + 2)$ is a factor.

	1	−3	−4	+12
−2		−2	10	−12
	1	−5	+6	0

Hence $f(x) = (x + 2)(x^2 - 5x + 6)$
$= (x + 2)(x - 3)(x - 2)$

9. By Pythagoras' theorem the 3rd side of the triangle $= \sqrt{3^2 + 7^2} = \sqrt{58}$

$$\cos A = \frac{7}{\sqrt{58}} \qquad \cos 2A = 2\cos^2 A - 1$$

$$= 2\left(\frac{7}{\sqrt{58}}\right)^2 - 1$$

$$= 2\left(\frac{49}{58}\right) - 1$$

$$= \frac{98}{58} - \frac{58}{58} = \frac{40}{58} = \frac{20}{29}$$

$$\cos 2A = \frac{20}{29}$$

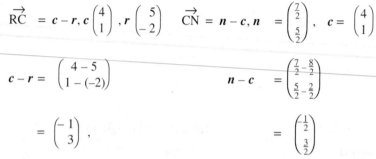

10. $f(x) = (2x^2 - x)^5$
By chain rule method
$f'(x) = 5(2x^2 - x)^4(4x - 1)$
$f'(x) = 5(4x - 1)(2x^2 - x)^4$

11.

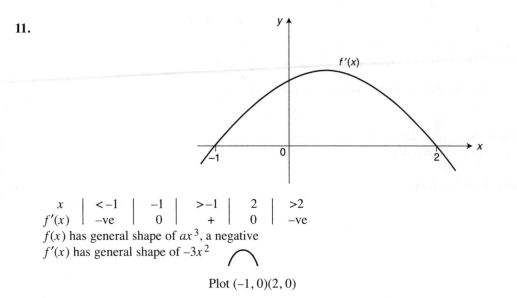

x	<-1	-1	>-1	2	>2
$f'(x)$	$-$ve	0	$+$	0	$-$ve

$f(x)$ has general shape of ax^3, a negative
$f'(x)$ has general shape of $-3x^2$

Plot $(-1, 0)(2, 0)$

12. $C = 3\cos\left(x + \dfrac{\pi}{3}\right)$ maximum value $=$ 3 when $x + \dfrac{\pi}{3} = 0$ or 2π

minimum value $= -3$ when $x + \dfrac{\pi}{3} = \pi$

min, $x + \dfrac{\pi}{3} = \pi$, $x = \pi - \dfrac{\pi}{3}$, $x = \dfrac{2\pi}{3}$ max, $x = -\dfrac{\pi}{3}$ or $2\pi - \dfrac{\pi}{3} = \dfrac{5\pi}{3}$

$x = \dfrac{5\pi}{3}$ $y = 3$, $x = \dfrac{2\pi}{3}$ $y = -3$

1. (a) Using synthetic division

$$x^3 - 3x^2 - 6x + 8$$

$x = -2$	1	-3	-6	8
		-2	10	-8
	1	-5	4	0

Remainder $= 0$; $f(-2) = 0$

Since the remainder $= 0$, -2 is a root and $(x + 2)$ is a factor

$$x^3 - 3x^2 - 6x + 8 = (x + 2)(x^2 - 5x + 4)$$

By factorising the second bracket further . . . $f(x) = (x + 2)(x - 1)(x - 4)$

(b) $f(x)$ meets the x-axis when $y = 0$; $(x + 2)(x - 1)(x - 4) = 0$
$(x + 2) = 0$ or $(x - 1) = 0$ or $(x - 4) = 0$
$x = -2, x = 1, x = 4$
coordinates are $(-2, 0)(1, 0)(4, 0)$

$f(x)$ meets the y-axis when $x = 0$; $f(0) = 8$; coordinates are $(0, 8)$

Hence $f(x)$ meets the axes at the points $(-2, 0), (1, 0), (4, 0), (0, 8)$

2. (a) $a = \begin{pmatrix} 1 \\ -2 \\ 4 \end{pmatrix}$ $b = \begin{pmatrix} -2 \\ 4 \\ 1 \end{pmatrix}$ $\overrightarrow{AP} : \overrightarrow{PB} = 2 : 1$

By section formula method

$$P = \frac{1}{3}(a + 2b) = \frac{1}{3}\left[\begin{pmatrix} 1 \\ -2 \\ 4 \end{pmatrix} + \begin{pmatrix} -4 \\ 8 \\ 2 \end{pmatrix}\right] = \frac{1}{3}\begin{pmatrix} -3 \\ 6 \\ 6 \end{pmatrix}$$

$$P = (-1, 2, 2)$$

(b) $\overrightarrow{BP} = -\overrightarrow{PB}$

hence $\overrightarrow{AP} : \overrightarrow{BP}$

$= \overrightarrow{AP} : -\overrightarrow{PB}$

$= 2 : -1$

$\overrightarrow{AP} : \overrightarrow{BP} = 2 : -1$

* For Alternative Method see *
Paper A Question 11 and Paper C Question 7

3. L(2, 4), M(−1, −2), N(3, 7)

$$m_{MN} = \frac{7 - (-2)}{3 - (-1)} = \frac{9}{4}$$

$m_{MN} \cdot m_{LQ} = -1$ for LQ $\sqsubset\!\sqcap\!\sqsupset$ to MN

Hence $m_{LQ} = -\dfrac{4}{9}$ through point L(2, 4)

$$y - 4 = -\frac{4}{9}(x - 2)$$

$$9y - 36 = -4x + 8$$

$$9y + 4x = 44 = \text{equation of LQ.}$$

4. (a) $x^2 + y^2 - 6x + 8y + 9 = 0$, $C(-g, -f)$, $r = \sqrt{g^2 + f^2 - 9}$

$2g = -6$, $-g = 3$,

$2f = 8$, $-f = -4$

Centre $= (3, -4)$, radius $= \sqrt{3^2 + 4^2 - 9} = \sqrt{25 - 9} = \sqrt{16}$

Radius $= 4$

(b) After reflection in x-axis $\qquad\qquad (3, -4) \rightarrow (3, 4)$

Radius unchanged.

Equation is $x^2 + y^2 - 6x - 8y + 9 = 0$

* For Alternative Method see *
Paper B Question 3(b)

5. (a) $f(x) = 4x^3 + mx$

$f'(x) = 12x^2 + m = m \tan = 0$ $\qquad$ {m tan is the gradient of the tangent to the curve.}

$x = \pm\dfrac{\sqrt{3}}{2}$ $\quad 12\left(\dfrac{\sqrt{3}}{2}\right)^2 + m = 0$ $\qquad$ {m tan $= 0$ for stationary values.}

$$12\left(\frac{3}{4}\right) + m = 0$$

$$9 + m = 0, \Rightarrow m = -9$$

(b) Hence $f(x) = 4x^3 - 9x$

and $f(-2) = 4(-2)^3 - 9(-2)$

$\Rightarrow 4(-8) + 18$

$\Rightarrow -32 + 18$

$f(-2) = -14$

6. $(2\sqrt{3} - 5\sqrt{2})^2 = (2\sqrt{3}) - 5\sqrt{2})(2\sqrt{3} - 5\sqrt{2})$

$= 2\sqrt{3}(2\sqrt{3} - 5\sqrt{2}) - 5\sqrt{2}(2\sqrt{3} - 5\sqrt{2})$

$= 12 - 10\sqrt{6} - 10\sqrt{6} + 50$

$= 62 - 20\sqrt{6}$

7.

$$f(x) = \frac{x^3 + 2x^2 - 3x - 1}{3x^2}$$

$$f(x) = \frac{x^3}{3x^2} + \frac{2x^2}{3x^2} - \frac{3x}{3x^2} - \frac{1}{3x^2}$$

$$f(x) = \frac{x}{3} + \frac{2}{3} - \frac{1}{x} - \frac{1}{3x^2}$$

$$f(x) = \frac{x}{3} + \frac{2}{3} - x^{-1} - \frac{x^{-2}}{3}$$

We can now differentiate

$$f'(x) = \frac{1}{3} + x^{-2} + \frac{2x^{-3}}{3}$$

$$f'(x) = \frac{1}{3} + \frac{1}{x^2} + \frac{2}{3x^3}$$

8.

$$f(x) = x^3 - 5x^2 - x + d \qquad\qquad \text{If } f(-1) = 0, \text{ then } (x + 1) \text{ is a factor.}$$

$$
\begin{array}{r|rrrr}
 & 1 & -5 & -1 & d \\
-1 & & -1 & 6 & -5 \\
\hline
 & 1 & -6 & 5 & -5 + d, \; d - 5 = 0, \; d = 5
\end{array}
$$

Hence
$$f(x) = (x + 1)(x^2 - 6x + 5)$$
$$f(x) = (x + 1)(x - 1)(x - 5) \text{ fully factorised.}$$

9. *(a)* $u_{r+1} = mu_r + c,\; u_0 = 3,\; u_1 = 2,\; u_2 = 4$

$$u_1 = mu_0 + c \Rightarrow 2 = 3m + c \qquad\qquad ①$$
$$u_2 = mu_1 + c \Rightarrow 4 = 2m + c \qquad\qquad ②$$
$$② - ① \quad 2 = -m$$

Substitute $\quad m = -2$ in ①, $\qquad 2 = 3(-2) + c$
$$\Rightarrow 2 = -6 + c$$
$$c = 8$$

$$m = -2 \quad c = 8$$
$$u_{r+1} = -2u_r + 8$$

(b) $u_3 = -2u_2 + 8$
$$= -2(4) + 8 = 0$$

u_{-1} is found by using $u_0 = -2u_{-1} + 8,\, u_0 = 3$
$$3 = -2u_{-1} + 8$$
$$-5 = -2u_{-1}$$

$$\frac{5}{2} = u^{-1}$$

Hence $u_3 = 0,\; u_{-1} = \dfrac{5}{2}$

(c) $u_r = u_{r+1} \quad \Rightarrow \quad u_r = -2u_r + 8$
$$\Rightarrow 3u_r = 8$$
$$u_r = \frac{8}{3} \qquad \text{Check } -2\left(\frac{8}{3}\right) + 8 = \frac{-16}{3} + \frac{24}{3} = \frac{8}{3}$$

$$(u_r, u_{r+1}), \left(\frac{8}{3}, \frac{8}{3}\right)$$

10. (a) $f(x) = 2x^2 + 6x + p$ in form $ax^2 + bx + c$

    $a = 2$, $b = 6$, $c = p$, and using the discriminant $b^2 - 4ac = 0$ if $f(x)$ has equal roots

$$b^2 - 4ac = (6)^2 - 4(2)(p) = 0$$
$$36 - 8p = 0$$
$$8p = 36$$
$$p = \frac{36}{8} \; ; \; p = 4{\cdot}5$$

substitute $p = 4{\cdot}5$ into $f(x)$

$f(x) = 2x^2 + 6x + 4{\cdot}5$,

$a = 2$, $b = 6$, $c = 4{\cdot}5$,

and using the discriminant $b^2 - 4ac = 0$

if $f(x)$ has equal roots

$$b^2 - 4ac = (6)^2 - 4(2)(4{\cdot}5) = 0$$
$$36 - 36 = 0$$

root is $\dfrac{-b}{2a} \; ; \; = \dfrac{-6}{4} \; ; \; = \dfrac{-3}{2}$ or $-1{\cdot}5$

(b) coordinates of the root $= (-1{\cdot}5, 0)$

(c) y-intercept $= (0, 9)$, x-intercept $= (-1{\cdot}5, 0)$

11. $\displaystyle\int_{\pi/3}^{\pi/2} \sin x \, dx = \left[-\cos x \right]_{\pi/3}^{\pi/2}$

$(\pi/2)$ radians $= 90°$
$(\pi/3)$ radians $= 60°$

$$F(\pi/2) - F(\pi/3) = (-\cos \pi/2) - (-\cos \pi/3)$$
$$= 0 - (-0{\cdot}5)$$
$$= 0{\cdot}5$$

12. $4 \sin 2x - 2 = 0$

$4 \sin 2x = 2$

$\sin 2x = \dfrac{2}{4}$

$= 0{\cdot}5$

$\sin^{-1}(0{\cdot}5) = 30$ in quadrant 1 and $180 - 30$ in quadrant 2

$2x = 30°$ or $150°$

$x = 15°$ or $75°$

Period of $\sin 2x = \dfrac{360}{2} = 180°$ (i.e., 2 cycles in $360°$) add 180 to each of 15, and 75.

Hence x has 4 possible values, $15°$, $75°$, $195°$ and $255°$.

1. $(5 + 2\sqrt{3})^2 = (5 + 2\sqrt{3})(5 + 2\sqrt{3})$

$\qquad\qquad = 5(5 + 2\sqrt{3}) + 2\sqrt{3}(5 + 2\sqrt{3})$

$\qquad\qquad = 25 + 10\sqrt{3} + 10\sqrt{3} + 12$

$\qquad\qquad = 37 + 20\sqrt{3}$

2. $\cos 4x \qquad\qquad 0 \leq x \leq 180 \qquad\qquad \cos 4x = 0 \Rightarrow 4x = 90, 270$

$\text{period} = \dfrac{360}{4} = 90 \qquad\qquad\qquad 4x = 90, x = 22\frac{1}{2}, 112\frac{1}{2}$

$\qquad\qquad\qquad\qquad\qquad\qquad\qquad 4x = 270, x = 67\frac{1}{2}, 157\frac{1}{2}$

repeats twice in 180° $\qquad\qquad$ cuts at $x = \{22\frac{1}{2}, 67\frac{1}{2}, 112\frac{1}{2}, 157\frac{1}{2}\}$

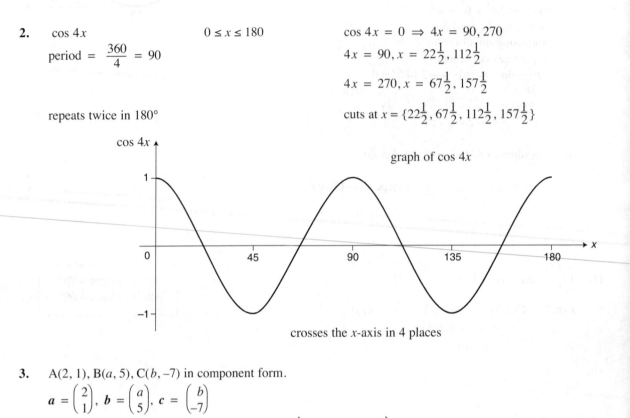

graph of $\cos 4x$

crosses the x-axis in 4 places

3. A(2, 1), B(a, 5), C(b, –7) in component form.

$$\boldsymbol{a} = \begin{pmatrix} 2 \\ 1 \end{pmatrix}, \; \boldsymbol{b} = \begin{pmatrix} a \\ 5 \end{pmatrix}, \; \boldsymbol{c} = \begin{pmatrix} b \\ -7 \end{pmatrix}$$

If points are collinear, B is a shared point and $\overrightarrow{AB}$ is parallel to $\overrightarrow{BC}$.

$\Rightarrow \boldsymbol{b} - \boldsymbol{a} = k(\boldsymbol{c} - \boldsymbol{b})$

$$\boldsymbol{b} - \boldsymbol{a} = \begin{pmatrix} a - 2 \\ 4 \end{pmatrix}, \; \boldsymbol{c} - \boldsymbol{b} = \begin{pmatrix} b - a \\ -12 \end{pmatrix}$$

If collinear, ratio is $4 : -12 = 1 : -3$

$\qquad \Rightarrow -3(a - 2) = b - a$

$\qquad\qquad -3a + 6 = b - a$

$\qquad \Rightarrow \qquad 6 = 2a + b$

<u>Alternative method</u>

A(2, 1), B(a, 5), C(b, –7)

$m_{AB} = \dfrac{5 - 1}{a - 2}, \; m_{BC} = \dfrac{5 - (-7)}{a - b}$

$\dfrac{4}{a - 2} = \dfrac{12}{a - b}$ if parallel

$4a - 4b = 12a - 24$

$\Rightarrow 24 = 8a + 4b \Rightarrow 6 = 2a + b$ as given.

4. General equation of a circle is $x^2 + y^2 + 2gx + 2fy + c = 0$

Centre $= (-g, -f)$, $\quad r = \sqrt{g^2 + f^2 - c}$

Given equation $= x^2 + y^2 - 8x + 6y + 21 = 0$

$2g = -8, \Rightarrow -g = 4, \; 2f = 6 \Rightarrow -f = -3$

Radius $= \sqrt{4^2 + 3^2 - 21} = \sqrt{4} = 2$

Centre $= (4, -3)$ reflected in $y = -x$ becomes $(3, -4), r = 2$.

Hence equation of circle after reflection in $y = -x$:
$$x^2 + y^2 - 6x + 8y + 21 = 0$$

5. By Pythagoras' Theorem $\quad\quad AB = \sqrt{(2\sqrt{2})^2 + 1^2} = 3$

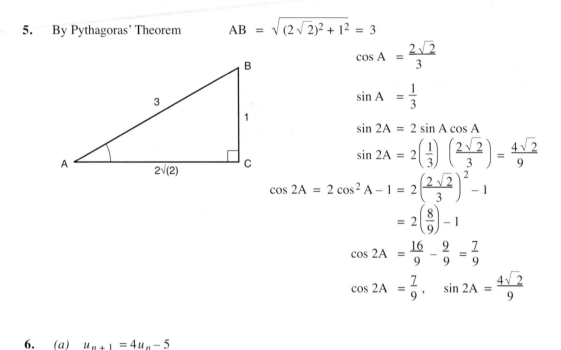

$$\cos A = \frac{2\sqrt{2}}{3}$$

$$\sin A = \frac{1}{3}$$

$$\sin 2A = 2 \sin A \cos A$$

$$\sin 2A = 2\left(\frac{1}{3}\right)\left(\frac{2\sqrt{2}}{3}\right) = \frac{4\sqrt{2}}{9}$$

$$\cos 2A = 2\cos^2 A - 1 = 2\left(\frac{2\sqrt{2}}{3}\right)^2 - 1$$

$$= 2\left(\frac{8}{9}\right) - 1$$

$$\cos 2A = \frac{16}{9} - \frac{9}{9} = \frac{7}{9}$$

$$\cos 2A = \frac{7}{9}, \quad \sin 2A = \frac{4\sqrt{2}}{9}$$

6. (a) $u_{n+1} = 4u_n - 5$

$u_{n+2} = 4u_{n+1} - 5$

$\quad\quad\;\; = 4(4u_n - 5) - 5$

$u_{n+2} = 16u_n - 25$

(b) $\quad u_{n+1} \quad = 4u_n - 5$

$\quad\quad u_{n+3} \quad = 4u_{n+2} - 5$

$\quad\quad\quad\quad\quad = 4(16u_n - 25) - 5$

$\quad\quad u_{n+3} \quad = 64u_n - 105$

$\quad\quad u_{n+3} \quad = 87$

$\quad 64u_n - 105 = 87$

$\quad 64u_n \quad\quad = 192$

$\quad\quad u_n \quad\quad = 3$

(c) Find u_{n-1} $\quad\quad u_n = 4u_{n-1} - 5$

$\quad\quad\quad\quad\quad\quad\quad\quad 3 = 4u_{n-1} - 5$

$\quad\quad\quad\quad\quad 4u_{n-1} = 8; \quad u_{n-1} = 2$

Find u_{n+4} $\quad\quad u_{n+4} = 4u_{n+3} - 5$

$\quad\quad\quad\quad\quad\quad\quad\quad = 4(87) - 5$

$\quad\quad\quad\quad\quad u_{n+4} = 343$

7. $f(x) = (3x^2 - 2x)^4$

By chain rule method:

$$
\begin{aligned}
f'(x) &= 4(3x^2 - 2x)^3(6x - 2) \\
&= 4(6x - 2)(3x^2 - 2x)^3 \\
f'(x) &= 4(6x - 2)(3x^2 - 2x)^3 \\
f'(-1) &= 4(6(-1) - 2)(3(-1)^2 - 2(-1))^3 \\
f'(-1) &= 4(-6 - 2)(3 + 2)^3 \\
&= 4(-8)(5)^3 \\
f'(-1) &= -32 \times 125 \\
&= -4000
\end{aligned}
$$

8. $D = 2\cos\left(x - \dfrac{\pi}{2}\right)$ minimum value $= -2$ when $x - \dfrac{\pi}{2} = \pi$

$$\Rightarrow \quad x = \pi + \frac{\pi}{2} = \frac{3\pi}{2}$$

maximum value $= 2$ when $\left(x - \dfrac{\pi}{2}\right) = 0$ or 2π,

$$x = \frac{\pi}{2} \text{ or } \frac{5\pi}{2} \text{ (too large)}$$

$$(x, y) = \left(\frac{\pi}{2}, 2\right), \left(\frac{3\pi}{2}, -2\right)$$

9. $f(x) = ax^3$, a +ve

$f'(x) = 3ax^2 \Rightarrow$ shape $\smile$

x	<-3	-3	>-3	0	>0
$f'(x)$	$+$	0	$-$	0	$+$
Plot	above	on	below	on	above

Points in relation to x-axis.

Plot $(-3, 0)(0, 0)$

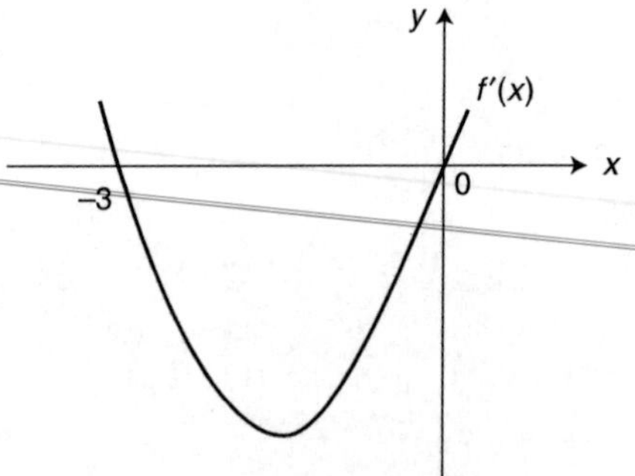

10. *(a)*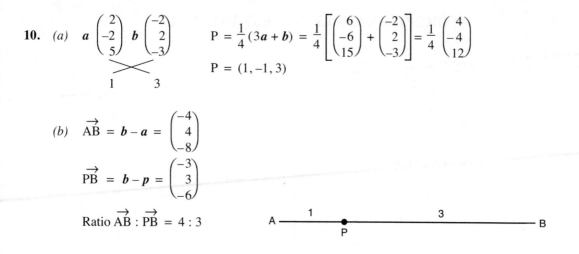

$a \begin{pmatrix} 2 \\ -2 \\ 5 \end{pmatrix}$ $b \begin{pmatrix} -2 \\ 2 \\ -3 \end{pmatrix}$ $P = \frac{1}{4}(3a + b) = \frac{1}{4}\left[\begin{pmatrix} 6 \\ -6 \\ 15 \end{pmatrix} + \begin{pmatrix} -2 \\ 2 \\ -3 \end{pmatrix}\right] = \frac{1}{4}\begin{pmatrix} 4 \\ -4 \\ 12 \end{pmatrix}$

$P = (1, -1, 3)$

(b) $\overrightarrow{AB} = b - a = \begin{pmatrix} -4 \\ 4 \\ -8 \end{pmatrix}$

$\overrightarrow{PB} = b - p = \begin{pmatrix} -3 \\ 3 \\ -6 \end{pmatrix}$

Ratio $\overrightarrow{AB} : \overrightarrow{PB} = 4 : 3$

11. $f'(x) = 3x^2 - 4x + 5$ $\qquad f(x)$ passes through $(-2, 6)$

$f(x) = \int (3x^2 - 4x + 5)dx = x^3 - 2x^2 + 5x + c$ from the given point, when $x = -2, f(x) = 6,$

therefore, $(-2)^3 - 2(-2)^2 + 5(-2) + c = 6; \ c = 32$

Hence, $\qquad f(x) = x^3 - 2x^2 + 5x + 32$

and $\qquad f(3) = (3)^3 - 2(3)^2 + 5(3) + 32; \ = 27 - 18 + 15 + 32 = 56$

$\qquad f(3) = 56$

12. Let given points be P, Q, R respectively.

$\qquad (2, 5) \qquad (4, 1) \qquad (8, -3)$
$\qquad\quad P \qquad\quad Q \qquad\quad R$

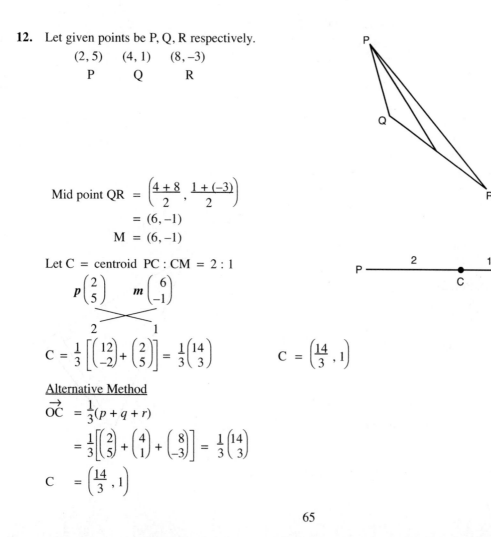

Mid point QR $= \left(\dfrac{4 + 8}{2}, \dfrac{1 + (-3)}{2}\right)$

$\qquad\qquad\qquad = (6, -1)$

$\qquad\qquad\quad M = (6, -1)$

Let C = centroid PC : CM = 2 : 1

$p\begin{pmatrix} 2 \\ 5 \end{pmatrix}$ $m\begin{pmatrix} 6 \\ -1 \end{pmatrix}$

$C = \frac{1}{3}\left[\begin{pmatrix} 12 \\ -2 \end{pmatrix} + \begin{pmatrix} 2 \\ 5 \end{pmatrix}\right] = \frac{1}{3}\begin{pmatrix} 14 \\ 3 \end{pmatrix}$ $\qquad C = \left(\dfrac{14}{3}, 1\right)$

Alternative Method

$\overrightarrow{OC} = \frac{1}{3}(p + q + r)$

$\qquad = \frac{1}{3}\left[\begin{pmatrix} 2 \\ 5 \end{pmatrix} + \begin{pmatrix} 4 \\ 1 \end{pmatrix} + \begin{pmatrix} 8 \\ -3 \end{pmatrix}\right] = \frac{1}{3}\begin{pmatrix} 14 \\ 3 \end{pmatrix}$

$C \qquad = \left(\dfrac{14}{3}, 1\right)$

1. $\int_a^2 (x^2 - 1)\,dx = 0 \Rightarrow \left[\dfrac{x^3}{3} - x\right]_a^2 = 0$

$$\left(\dfrac{8}{3} - 2\right) - \left(\dfrac{a^3}{3} - a\right) = 0$$

$$\dfrac{8-6}{3} - \dfrac{a^3}{3} + a = 0$$

$$\dfrac{2}{3} - \dfrac{a^3}{3} + a = 0$$

$$\Rightarrow \quad a - \dfrac{a^3}{3} = -\dfrac{2}{3}$$

$$3a - a^3 = -2$$

$$a(3 - a^2) = -2$$

$$a(a^2 - 3) = 2$$

$$a = -1$$

> By trial and error since $a < 2$,
> try $1, 0, -1$ and find that
> $$-1((-1)^2 - 3)$$
> $$= -1(1 - 3)$$
> $$= -1(-2)$$
> $$= 2$$

Alternative Method:

$$3a - a^3 = -2$$

By synthetic division $\quad \Rightarrow \quad 3a - a^3 + 2 = 0$

$$\Rightarrow \quad a^3 - 3a - 2 = 0$$

$a^3 - 0a^2 - 3a - 2$

	1	0	−3	−2
−1		−1	1	2
	1	−1	−2	0

factors $(x + 1)(x^2 - x - 2) = (x + 1)(x + 1)(x - 2)$

$$x = -1 \text{ or } x = 2$$

Hence $a = -1$

2. $f(x) = 0 \Rightarrow x(x^2 - 3)(x^2 + 4)(x^2 - 1) = 0$

$$x = 0, \qquad x = \pm\sqrt{3}, \qquad x = \pm 1$$

Note: $x^2 + 4 = 0 \Rightarrow x^2 = -4$ no real roots $x \notin R$

s.s. $\{-\sqrt{3}, -1, 0, \sqrt{3}, 1\}$

3. P(−2, 5), Q(2, −1), R(4, 2)

$$m_{PR} = \dfrac{5 - 2}{-2 - 4} = \dfrac{3}{-6} = -\dfrac{1}{2}$$

$m_{PR} \cdot m_{AQ} = -1$ if AQ ⊢ PR

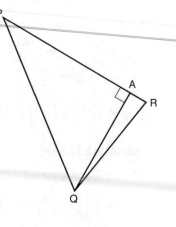

$$m_1 m_2 = -1 \qquad m_1 = -\dfrac{1}{2}, \quad m_2 = 2, \text{ through Q}(2, -1)$$

$$y + 1 = 2(x - 2)$$

$$y + 1 = 2x - 4$$

$$y = 2x - 5 \text{ is equation of altitude.}$$

4.

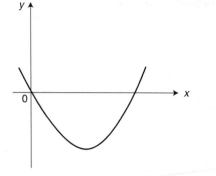

Graph of $6 + x - x^2$

(i) coefficient of x^2
negative $\Rightarrow$ shape

(ii) $ax^2 + bx + c$ cuts y at $(0, c)$
$c = 6$, point $(0, 6)$

2 main reasons why graph is not $f(x)$
$f(x) = ax^2 + bx + c$
    $a < 0$ parabola should be inverted
    c +ve $(0, c)$ should cut y at $(0, 6)$

5. General equation of a circle $\quad x^2 + y^2 + 2gx + 2fy + c = 0$
$x^2 + y^2 + 12x - 4y + 15 = 0$
$2g = 12, \ -g = -6, \ 2f = -4, \ -f = 2$
Centre $= (-g, -f), \quad r = \sqrt{g^2 + f^2 - c}$
Centre $= (-6, 2) \quad r = \sqrt{6^2 + 2^2 - 15} = \sqrt{25} = 5.$
Hence circle has centre $(-6, 2)$ radius 5.

6. $\qquad \log a + \log b = \log (ab); \quad \log a - \log b = \log \left(\dfrac{a}{b}\right)$
Hence $\quad \log a + \log b - \log c = \log \left(\dfrac{ab}{c}\right)$

$\log_{10} 40 + \log_{10} 20 - \log_{10} 80$
$= \log_{10}((40 \times 20) \div 80)$
$= \log_{10} 10$
$= 1$

7. $\qquad x^3 - 3x^2 - x + a$, if divisible by $(x - 3)$ then $f(3) = 0 \quad$ by synthetic division

	1	−3	−1	a	
$x = 3$		3	0	−3	(Remainder = 0)
	1	0	−1	0 ,	$\Rightarrow \quad -3 + a = 0$
					$\Rightarrow \qquad a = 3$

$a = 3$

$\qquad f(x) = x^3 - 3x^2 - x + 3$
$\qquad f(x) = (x - 3)(x^2 - 1)$
$\Rightarrow \quad f(x) = (x - 1)(x + 1)(x - 3)$ fully factorised.

8. For function to have equal roots, discriminant $= 0$, discriminant $= b^2 - 4ac$

$$3x^2 - 2x - c$$

$$b^2 - 4ac = 0$$

$$a = 3, \ b = -2, \ c = -c$$

$$b^2 - 4ac = 0 \Rightarrow (-2)^2 - 4(3)(-c) = 0$$

$$\Rightarrow \qquad 4 + 12c = 0$$

$$\Rightarrow \qquad 12c = -4$$

$$\Rightarrow \qquad c = \frac{-4}{12} = -\frac{1}{3}$$

Equation is

$$3x^2 - 2x + \frac{1}{3} \quad \text{or} \quad \frac{1}{3}(9x^2 - 6x + 1) = \frac{1}{3}(3x - 1)^2$$

9.

$$\overrightarrow{OP} = p \qquad \overrightarrow{OQ} = q$$

$P = (1, 4, -1), \ Q = (1, -2, 3)$

$$p = \begin{pmatrix} 1 \\ 4 \\ -1 \end{pmatrix} \qquad q = \begin{pmatrix} 1 \\ -2 \\ 3 \end{pmatrix}$$

$$p \cdot q = (1 \times 1) + (4 \times (-2)) + (-1 \times 3)$$

$$= 1 - 8 - 3 = -10$$

$$|p| = \sqrt{1^2 + 4^2 + (-1)^2}$$

$$= \sqrt{18}$$

$$|q| = \sqrt{1^2 + (-2)^2 + 3^2}$$

$$= \sqrt{14}$$

$$\frac{\overrightarrow{OP} \cdot \overrightarrow{OQ}}{|p||q|} = \cos P\hat{O}Q$$

$$= \frac{-10}{\sqrt{18}\ \sqrt{14}}$$

10. (a) $u_{r+1} = mu_r + c, \ u_0 = 2, \ u_1 = -1, \ u_2 = 14$

$$u_1 = m(u_0) + c \Rightarrow -1 = 2m + c \qquad \qquad ①$$

$$u_2 = m(u_1) + c \Rightarrow 14 = -m + c \qquad \qquad ②$$

$$② - ① \quad 15 = -3m \Rightarrow m = -5$$

Substitute $m = -5$ in ①, $\qquad -1 = 2(-5) + c$

$$-1 = -10 + c$$

$$9 = c$$

$$m = -5, \ c = 9, \Rightarrow u_{r+1} = -5u_r + 9$$

(b) $u_3 = -5u_2 + 9$

$$= -5(14) + 9$$

$$= -70 + 9$$

$$u_3 = -61$$

To find u_{-1} use $u_0 = -5u_{-1} + 9, \ u_0 = 2$

$$2 = -5u_{-1} + 9$$

$$-7 = -5u_{-1}$$

$$\frac{7}{5} = u_{-1}$$

(c)   To find $u_r = u_{r+1} \Rightarrow u_r = -5u_r + 9$
$$\Rightarrow 6u_r = 9$$
$$u_r = \frac{9}{6}, = \frac{3}{2}$$

Check $-5\left(\frac{3}{2}\right) + 9 = -\frac{15}{2} + \frac{18}{2} = \frac{3}{2}$

$(u_r, u_{r+1}) = \left(\frac{3}{2}, \frac{3}{2}\right)$

---

11. $f(x) = 3 \sin(2x + 30°)$ let $x = 2x + 30°$

Sin x has maximum value   1 when $x = 90°$ maximum of 3 sin $x = 3$

Sin x has minimum value -1 when $x = 270°$ minimum of 3 sin $x = -3$

For maximum, $2x + 30 = 90$; $2x = 60$; $x = 30$

For minimum, $2x + 30 = 270$; $2x = 240$; $x = 120$

Period of the graph $= \dfrac{360}{2} = 180$ (add 180 to 30 and 120)

$f(x)$ has 2 maximum turning points $(30°, 3)$ and $(210°, 3)$

$f(x)$ has 2 minimum turning points $(120°, -3)$ and $(300°, -3)$

---

12. $2 \sin 2x + 1 = 0$

$2 \sin 2x = -1$

$\sin 2x = -\dfrac{1}{2}; = -0.5$

$\sin^{-1}(0.5) = 30$ in quadrant 1, sin is negative in quadrants 3 and 4

In quadrant 3 angle $= 180 + 30$

In quadrant 4 angle $= 360 - 30$

$2x = 210°$ or $330°$

$x = 105°$ or $165°$

Period of sin $2x = \dfrac{360}{2} = 180°$ (i.e., 2 cycles in 360°) add 180 to each of 105 and 165.

Hence x has 4 possible values $105°$, $165°$, $285°$ and $345°$.

1.

$$x^3 + 4x^2 + x - t$$

If divisible by $x + 2$ then $f(-2) = 0$

$$
\begin{array}{r|rrrr}
-2 & 1 & 4 & 1 & -t \\
   &   & -2 & -4 & 6 \\
\hline
   & 1 & 2 & -3 & 6 - t
\end{array}
\Rightarrow 6 - t = 0 \Rightarrow t = 6
$$

$$t = 6, \Rightarrow \quad 1 \quad\quad 2 \quad\quad -3 \quad\quad 0$$

$f(x) = (x + 2)(x^2 + 2x - 3)$

$f(x) = (x + 2)(x + 3)(x - 1)$ fully factorised.

2. By Pythagoras' theorem

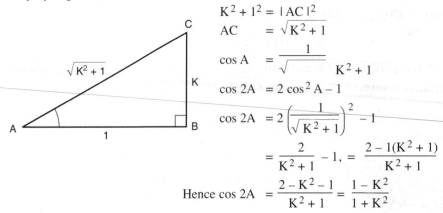

$$K^2 + 1^2 = |AC|^2$$

$$AC = \sqrt{K^2 + 1}$$

$$\cos A = \frac{1}{\sqrt{K^2 + 1}}$$

$$\cos 2A = 2\cos^2 A - 1$$

$$\cos 2A = 2\left(\frac{1}{\sqrt{K^2 + 1}}\right)^2 - 1$$

$$= \frac{2}{K^2 + 1} - 1, = \frac{2 - 1(K^2 + 1)}{K^2 + 1}$$

Hence $\cos 2A = \dfrac{2 - K^2 - 1}{K^2 + 1} = \dfrac{1 - K^2}{1 + K^2}$

3 *(a)* General equation of a circle $x^2 + y^2 + 2gx + 2fy + c = 0$

centre $= (-g, -f)$, radius $= \sqrt{g^2 + f^2 - c}$

$x^2 + y^2 - 6x + 8y = 0$ centre $= (3, -4)$, $r = \sqrt{3^2 + (-4)^2} = 5$.

centre $(3, -4)$, radius $= 5$.

(b)

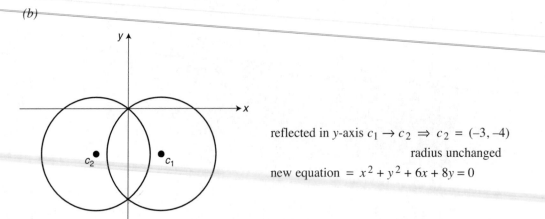

reflected in y-axis $c_1 \to c_2 \Rightarrow c_2 = (-3, -4)$

radius unchanged

new equation $= x^2 + y^2 + 6x + 8y = 0$

4. $\dfrac{2+x}{2} - (2-x) < 5$

$2 + x - 2(2-x) < 10$

$2 + x - 4 + 2x \; < 10$

$\qquad 3x - 2 < 10$

$\qquad\quad 3x < 12$

$\qquad\quad\; x < \; 4$

5. $f(x) \; = \; 3 \sin 2x$

$f'(x) \; = \; 6 \cos 2x$

$x \; = \; \dfrac{\pi}{6} \Rightarrow 6 \cos 2 \left(\dfrac{\pi}{6}\right)$

$\qquad = 6 \cos \left(\dfrac{\pi}{3}\right) = 6 \times \dfrac{1}{2} = 3$

$f'\left(\dfrac{\pi}{6}\right) \; = \; 3$

6. By Pythagoras' Theorem $\sqrt{2^2 + 1^2} = $ hypotenuse $= \sqrt{5}$ hypotenuse.

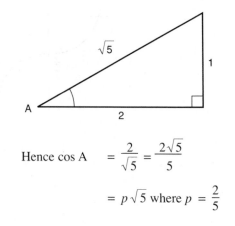

Hence $\cos A \quad = \dfrac{2}{\sqrt{5}} = \dfrac{2\sqrt{5}}{5}$

$\qquad\qquad\qquad = p\sqrt{5}$ where $p = \dfrac{2}{5}$

7.

$\qquad\qquad f(x) \; = \; (2x + \sqrt{x})^3$

$\qquad\qquad f(x) \; = \; (2x + x^{1/2})^3 \qquad$ (By chain rule method.)

$\qquad\qquad f'(x) = 3(2x + x^{1/2})^2 \left(2 + \dfrac{1}{2}x^{-1/2}\right)$

$\qquad\qquad\qquad = 3\left(2 + \dfrac{1}{2\sqrt{x}}\right)(2x + \sqrt{x})^2$

Hence $\qquad f'(x) = 3\left(2 + \dfrac{1}{2\sqrt{x}}\right)(2x + \sqrt{x})^2$

and $\qquad f'(4) = 3\left(2 + \dfrac{1}{2\sqrt{4}}\right)(2(4) + \sqrt{4})^2$

$\qquad\qquad\qquad = 3(2\tfrac{1}{4})(10)^2$

$\qquad\qquad\qquad = 3(225)$

$\qquad\qquad\qquad = 675$

8. $f(x) = x(x+2)(x^2-3)(x^2+1)(x^2-4) = 0$

Note: $x^2+1=0, \Rightarrow x^2 = -1,$ (not real) $x \notin R$

$\Rightarrow f(x) = 0, x = 0, x = -2, x = \pm\sqrt{3}, x = \pm 2$

Hence, S.S. $\{-\sqrt{3}, -2, 0, \sqrt{3}, 2\}$

9. $h(x) = g(f(x)) \quad g(x) = -x^2 + x + 2 \quad f(x) = 2x - 1$

$$
\begin{aligned}
g(f(x)) = g((2x-1)) &= -(2x-1)^2 + (2x-1) + 2 \\
&= -(4x^2 - 4x + 1) + 2x - 1 + 2 \\
&= -4x^2 + 4x - 1 + 2x + 1 \\
&= -4x^2 + 6x
\end{aligned}
$$

10.

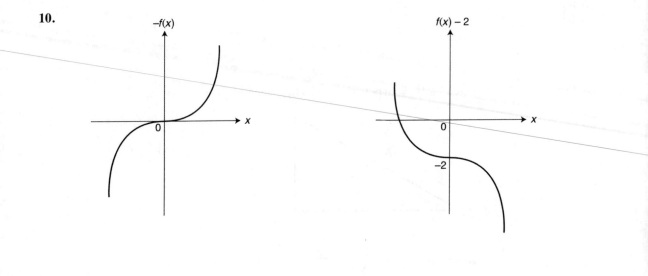

11. $\cos BAC = \dfrac{AB \cdot AC}{|AB||AC|}$

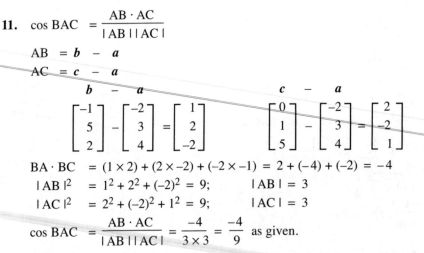

$AB = b - a$

$AC = c - a$

$$
\begin{array}{cc}
b - a & c - a \\
\begin{bmatrix} -1 \\ 5 \\ 2 \end{bmatrix} - \begin{bmatrix} -2 \\ 3 \\ 4 \end{bmatrix} = \begin{bmatrix} 1 \\ 2 \\ -2 \end{bmatrix} &
\begin{bmatrix} 0 \\ 1 \\ 5 \end{bmatrix} - \begin{bmatrix} -2 \\ 3 \\ 4 \end{bmatrix} = \begin{bmatrix} 2 \\ -2 \\ 1 \end{bmatrix}
\end{array}
$$

$BA \cdot BC = (1 \times 2) + (2 \times -2) + (-2 \times -1) = 2 + (-4) + (-2) = -4$

$|AB|^2 = 1^2 + 2^2 + (-2)^2 = 9; \qquad |AB| = 3$

$|AC|^2 = 2^2 + (-2)^2 + 1^2 = 9; \qquad |AC| = 3$

$\cos BAC = \dfrac{AB \cdot AC}{|AB||AC|} = \dfrac{-4}{3 \times 3} = \dfrac{-4}{9}$ as given.

Since the cosine of angle BAC is negative, the angle is in the second quadrant and is an obtuse angle.

12. (a) $3x^2 - 6x + 5 \quad = 3\left(x^2 - 2x + \dfrac{5}{3}\right) = 3\left((x^2 - 2x + 1) - 1 + \dfrac{5}{3}\right)$

$$= 3\left[(x-1)^2 - \dfrac{3}{3} + \dfrac{5}{3}\right]$$

$$= 3\left[(x-1)^2 + \dfrac{2}{3}\right]$$

$$= 3(x-1)^2 + 2$$

Alternative Method

$3x^2 - 6x + 5 = 3(x^2 - 2x) + 5 = 3[(x^2 - 2x + 1) - 1] + 5$

$\qquad\qquad\qquad\qquad\qquad\quad 3[(x-1)^2 - 1] + 5$

$\qquad\qquad\qquad\qquad\qquad\quad 3(x-1)^2 - 3 + 5$

$\qquad\qquad\qquad\qquad\quad = 3(x-1)^2 + 2$

Since the least value of any square number is 0,
then $(x-1)^2$ has minimum value 0.
Hence the minimum value of the function is $0 + 2$ when $x = 1$.
Minimum value of the function is $3(1-1)^2 + 2$ and the
coordinates of the minimum turning point $(1, 2)$.

(b) y-intersection $(0, 5)$, minimum turning point $(1, 2)$

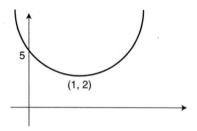

(c) Since the minimum turning point $(1, 2)$ lies above the x-axis, the curve does not cross the x-axis hence the equation has no real roots.

1. (a) $a = \begin{pmatrix} 3 \\ 1 \\ 3 \end{pmatrix}$ $b = \begin{pmatrix} -2 \\ 2 \\ -2 \end{pmatrix}$

$$P = \frac{1}{5}(3a + 2b) = \frac{1}{5}\left[\begin{pmatrix} 9 \\ 3 \\ 9 \end{pmatrix} + \begin{pmatrix} -4 \\ 4 \\ -4 \end{pmatrix}\right] = \frac{1}{5}\begin{pmatrix} 5 \\ 7 \\ 5 \end{pmatrix}$$

$$\begin{matrix} 2 & & 3 \end{matrix}$$

$$P = \left(1, \frac{7}{5}, 1\right)$$

2. $P(2, 7), Q(0, -1), R(-5, 4)$

$$m_{PQ} = \frac{7 - (-1)}{2 - 0} = \frac{8}{2} = 4$$

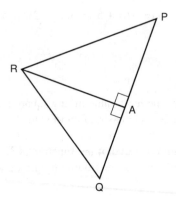

$$m_{PQ} \cdot m_{AR} = -1 \Rightarrow m_{AR} = -\frac{1}{4} \quad \text{through } R(-5, 4)$$

$$y - 4 = -\frac{1}{4}(x + 5)$$

$$4y - 16 = -x - 5$$

$$4y + x = 11 \text{ equation of altitude } AR$$

3. Let P, Q, R represent the given points $P(1, -1), Q(a, 2), R(b, 1)$.

$$p = \begin{pmatrix} 1 \\ -1 \end{pmatrix}, \quad q = \begin{pmatrix} a \\ 2 \end{pmatrix}, \quad r = \begin{pmatrix} b \\ 1 \end{pmatrix}$$

$\overrightarrow{PQ} = q - p$ $\qquad\qquad\qquad$ $\overrightarrow{QR} = r - q$

$\quad = \begin{pmatrix} a \\ 2 \end{pmatrix} - \begin{pmatrix} 1 \\ -1 \end{pmatrix}$ $\qquad\qquad$ $\quad = \begin{pmatrix} b \\ 1 \end{pmatrix} - \begin{pmatrix} a \\ 2 \end{pmatrix}$

$\quad = \begin{pmatrix} a - 1 \\ 3 \end{pmatrix}$ $\qquad\qquad\qquad$ $\quad = \begin{pmatrix} b - a \\ -1 \end{pmatrix}$

If collinear then vectors are parallel.

Hence $\begin{pmatrix} a - 1 \\ 3 \end{pmatrix} = \begin{pmatrix} b - a \\ -1 \end{pmatrix}$

$\qquad$ where $k = -3$

Hence $-3\begin{pmatrix} b - \\ -1 \end{pmatrix} = \begin{pmatrix} a - 1 \\ 3 \end{pmatrix}$

$\qquad \Rightarrow -3b + 3a = a - 1$

$\qquad \Rightarrow -3b + 2a = -1$

$\qquad \Rightarrow 3b - 2a = 1$

<u>Alternative Method:</u>

$P(1, -1), Q(a, 2), R(b, 1)$ Q is a shared point

$m_{PQ} = \dfrac{3}{a-1}$, $m_{QR} = \dfrac{1}{a-b}$

$m_{PQ} = m_{QR} \Rightarrow 3(a-b) = 1(a-1)$

$$3a - 3b = a - 1$$
$$2a = 3b - 1$$
$$1 = 3b - 2a$$
$$3b - 2a = 1$$

$\Rightarrow$ if collinear $3b - 2a = 1$

4. $4x^3 + mx = f(x)$

$f'(x) = 0$ for stationary value(s)

$f'(x) = 12x^2 + m = 0$

$$12x^2 = -m$$
$$x^2 = \dfrac{-m}{12}$$

$$x = \pm \dfrac{3}{2}, \left(-\dfrac{3}{2}\right)^2 = \left(\dfrac{3}{2}\right)^2$$

$x = \dfrac{3}{2}$, $\dfrac{9}{4} = \dfrac{-m}{12} \Rightarrow \dfrac{108}{4} = -m$, $27 = -m$, $m = -27$

Hence equation is $4x^3 - 27x$.

5.
$$\begin{aligned}
(2\sqrt{3} + 3\sqrt{2})^2 &= (2\sqrt{3} + 3\sqrt{2})(2\sqrt{3} + 3\sqrt{2}) \\
&= 2\sqrt{3}(2\sqrt{3} + 3\sqrt{2}) + 3\sqrt{2}(2\sqrt{3} + 3\sqrt{2}) \\
&= 12 + 6\sqrt{6} + 6\sqrt{6} + 18 \\
&= 30 + 12\sqrt{6}
\end{aligned}$$

6. $\displaystyle\int_{-3}^{0} (\text{upper} - \text{lower})\,dx \; + \int_{0}^{5} (\text{upper} - \text{lower})\,dx$

$\displaystyle = \int_{-3}^{0} (f_2(x) - f_1(x))\,dx \; + \int_{0}^{5} (f_1(x) - f_2(x))\,dx$

7.   *(a)* $u_{r+1} = Ku_r + t$ $u_0 = 0, u_1 = 2, u_2 = -4$

$u_1 \quad = Ku_0 + t \Rightarrow \quad 2 = t$

$u_2 \quad = Ku_1 + t \Rightarrow \; -4 = K(2) + t, t = 2$

$$-4 = 2K + 2$$
$$-6 = 2K$$

$t = 2, \quad K = -3$

$u_{r+1} = Ku_r + t \Rightarrow u_{r+1} = -3u_r + 2$

(b)

$$u_4 = -3u_3 + 2$$
$$u_3 = -3u_2 + 2$$
$$= -3(-4) + 2$$
$$u_3 = 14$$
Hence $u_4 = -3(14) + 2$
$$= -42 + 2$$
$$= -40$$

To find u_{-1} use $u_0 = -3u_{-1} + 2$
$$0 = -3u_{-1} + 2$$
$$-2 = -3u_{-1}$$
$$\frac{2}{3} = u_{-1}.$$

$$u_4 = -40$$
$$u_{-1} = \frac{2}{3}$$

8. $4x^2 + 4x + 5$

$$4\left(x^2 + x + \frac{5}{4}\right) = 4\left(x + \frac{1}{2}\right)^2 + 4\left(-\frac{1}{4} + \frac{5}{4}\right)$$
$$= 4\left(x + \frac{1}{2}\right)^2 + 4$$

Minimum value $= 4$ when $x = -\frac{1}{2}$

9. $y = 3x^2 - 2x + 1$

$\dfrac{dy}{dx} = 6x - 2 = m \tan$

parallel to $y = x - 3$
$$\Rightarrow m = 1$$
$$\Rightarrow 6x - 2 = 1$$
$$6x = 3$$

$$x = \frac{1}{2}, f\left(\frac{1}{2}\right) = 3\left(\frac{1}{2}\right)^2 - 2\left(\frac{1}{2}\right) + 1$$
$$\frac{3}{4} - 1 + 1 = \frac{3}{4}$$

Point $\left(\frac{1}{2}, \frac{3}{4}\right)$ $m = 1$

$$y - \frac{3}{4} = 1\left(x - \frac{1}{2}\right)$$
$$4y - 3 = 4\left(x - \frac{1}{2}\right)$$
$$4y - 3 = 4x - 2$$
$$4y - 4x = 1 \quad \text{or} \quad 4y = 4x + 1 \quad \text{(equation of the tangent)}$$

10. *(a)*

$$f(x) = 2x^2 - bx + 3 \text{ for equal roots } b^2 - 4ac = 0$$
$$a = 2, \quad b = -b, \quad c = 3$$
$$b^2 - 4ac = (-b)^2 - 4(2)(3)$$
$$b^2 - 24 = 0$$
$$b^2 = 24$$
$$b = \pm\sqrt{24}$$
$$b = 2\sqrt{6} \quad \text{or} \quad -2\sqrt{6}$$

(b) For real roots $b^2 - 4ac \geq 0$, $\quad 4ac = 24$

$$b \leq -2\sqrt{6} \quad \text{or} \quad b \geq 2\sqrt{6}$$

Since $(-b)^2 > 24$ for these values

then $b^2 - 4ac > 0$

(c) For no real roots

$$b^2 - 4ac < 0$$
$$\Rightarrow \quad b^2 - 24 < 0$$
$$b^2 < 24$$
$$-2\sqrt{6} < b < 2\sqrt{6}$$

(d) $f(x)$ cuts y-axis at $(0, 3)$

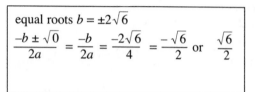

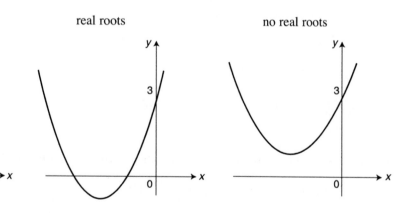

equal roots $b = \pm 2\sqrt{6}$

$$\frac{-b \pm \sqrt{0}}{2a} = \frac{-b}{2a} = \frac{-2\sqrt{6}}{4} = \frac{-\sqrt{6}}{2} \text{ or } \frac{\sqrt{6}}{2}$$

11. $\text{Sin } A = \dfrac{2}{3}$. Find the exact value of tan 2A.

$$\sqrt{9-4} = \sqrt{5}$$

opposite $= 2$

hypotenuse $= 3$

third side $= \sqrt{5}$

$\sin A = \dfrac{2}{3}$ and $\cos A = \dfrac{\sqrt{5}}{3}$

$\tan 2A = \dfrac{\sin 2A}{\cos 2A}$

$\sin 2A = 2\sin A \cos A \longrightarrow = 2 \cdot \left(\dfrac{2}{3}\right) \cdot \left(\dfrac{\sqrt{5}}{3}\right) \longrightarrow \dfrac{4\sqrt{5}}{9}$

$\cos 2A = \cos^2 A - \sin^2 A \longrightarrow = \left(\dfrac{\sqrt{5}}{3}\right)^2 - \left(\dfrac{2}{3}\right)^2 \longrightarrow \dfrac{1}{9}$

$\dfrac{\sin 2A}{\cos 2A} = \dfrac{\dfrac{4\sqrt{5}}{9}}{\dfrac{1}{9}} = 4\sqrt{5} = \tan 2A$

12. *(a)* $x^2 + y^2 - 10x + 2y + 1 = 0$;

centre $= (-g, -f)$;

$2g = -10$, $2f = 2$, centre $= (5, -1)$

(b) $C = (5, -1)$; $Q = (1, 2)$; $m_{CP} = \dfrac{2 - (-1)}{1 - 5} = \dfrac{3}{-4}$ $m_{\text{tangent}} \times m_{CP} = -1$

$\dfrac{3}{-4} \times \dfrac{4}{3} = -1$ hence $m_{\text{tangent}} = \dfrac{4}{3}$ through $P(1, 2) = (a, b)$

$y - b = m(x - a)$

$y - 2 = \dfrac{4}{3}(x - 1)$

$3y - 6 = 4(x - 1)$

$3y - 6 = 4x - 4$

$3y = 4x + 2$ is the equation of the tangent to the circle

(c) $3y = 4x + 2$; when $x = 0$, $y = \dfrac{2}{3}$; when $y = 0$, $4x + 2 = 0$, $x = -\dfrac{1}{2}$

Coordinates are $\left(0, \dfrac{2}{3}\right)$ and $\left(-\dfrac{1}{2}, 0\right)$

1. $f(x) = x^3 - 3x - 5$

$f'(x) = 3x^2 - 3 = m \ \tan = 0$ for S.V.

$\qquad 3(x^2 - 1) = 0$

$\qquad\qquad x = \pm 1$

x	$\rightarrow$	-1	$\rightarrow$	1	$\rightarrow$
$(x^2 - 1)$	$+$	0	$-$	0	$+$
$f'(x)$	$\nearrow$	$\rightarrow$	$\searrow$	$\rightarrow$	$\nearrow$

shape

$f'(x)$ decreasing $-1 < x < 1$

<u>Alternative Method</u>:

Using second derivative

$f''(x) = 6x$

$f''(-1)$ –ve $\qquad$ max T.P. $f(-1)$

$f''(1)$ +ve $\qquad$ min T.P. $f(1)$

$f(x)$ decreasing for $\{-1 < x < 1\}$

2. $3xy = -2$

$\quad y = \dfrac{-2}{3x} \qquad x = 1, y = -\dfrac{2}{3}, x = -1, y = \dfrac{2}{3}$

$\qquad\qquad P\left(1, -\dfrac{2}{3}\right), Q\left(-1, \dfrac{2}{3}\right)$

$\qquad\qquad m_{PQ} = \dfrac{\frac{4}{3}}{-2} = -\dfrac{4}{6} = -\dfrac{2}{3}$

$\qquad\qquad$ gradient of PQ $= -\dfrac{2}{3}$

3. $\qquad \cos 3x + \cos x$

$= \cos(2x + x) + \cos(2x - x)$

$= \cos 2x \cos x - \sin 2x \sin x$

$\quad + \cos 2x \cos x + \sin 2x \sin x$

$= 2 \cos 2x \cos x$

$\qquad$ Hence $\cos 3x + \cos x = 2 \cos 2x \cos x$.

4. $2x^2 + x + 2$

$$= 2\left(x^2 + \frac{1}{2}x + 1\right)$$

$$= 2\left(x + \frac{1}{4}\right)^2 + 2\left(-\frac{1}{16} + 1\right)$$

$$= 2\left(x + \frac{1}{4}\right)^2 + 2\left(\frac{15}{16}\right)$$

$$= 2\left(x + \frac{1}{4}\right)^2 + \frac{15}{8}$$

minimum value $= \frac{15}{8}$ when $x = -\frac{1}{4}$, $\left(-\frac{1}{4}, \frac{15}{8}\right)$ min. T.P.

5. $\dfrac{x - 2y}{3} = \dfrac{y - 2x}{2} \Rightarrow 2(x - 2y) = 3(y - 2x)$

$$2x - 4y = 3y - 6x$$
$$8x = 7y$$
$$x = \frac{7}{8}y$$

To find value of $\dfrac{7x - 2y}{3x + y}$

Substitude $x = \dfrac{7}{8}y$

$$= \frac{7\left(\dfrac{7}{8}\right)y - 2y}{3\left(\dfrac{7}{8}\right)y + y}$$

$$= \frac{\left(\dfrac{49}{8} - 2\right)y}{\left(\dfrac{21}{8} + 1\right)y} = \frac{\dfrac{49 - 16}{8}}{\dfrac{21 + 8}{8}} = \frac{33}{29}$$

Hence $\dfrac{7x - 2y}{3x + y} = \dfrac{33}{29}$

6. $f(x) = x^2 - 3, \ g(x) = 2 - x$

$$f(g(x)) = f(2 - x) = (2 - x)^2 - 3$$
$$= 4 - 4x + x^2 - 3$$
$$f(g(x)) = x^2 - 4x + 1$$
$$f(g(2)) = 2^2 - 4(2) + 1$$
$$= 4 - 8 + 1$$
$$= -3$$

Alternative Method:
$g(2) = 2 - 2 = 0$
$f(0) = 0^2 - 3 = -3$

7.

x	< 2	2	> 2
$f'(x)$	$+$	0	$-ve$
Plot	above	on	below

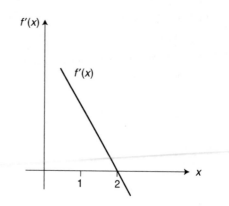

in relation to x-axis
intercepts x-axis at $(2, 0)$

⌢ shape $-x^2$ $\qquad$ $f'(x) \Rightarrow m$ is $-ve$ ↘

$f(x)$ quadratic, $f'(x)$ linear

8. $\displaystyle\int_1^4 \left(\sqrt{x} + \frac{1}{2\sqrt{x}}\right) dx = \int_1^4 \left(x^{1/2} + \frac{1}{2}(x)^{-1/2}\right) dx$

$$= \left[\frac{2x^{3/2}}{3} + x^{1/2}\right]_1^4$$

$$= \left(\frac{16}{3} + 2\right) - \left(\frac{2}{3} + 1\right)$$

$$= \frac{14}{3} + 1 = \frac{17}{3} \text{ or } 5\frac{2}{3}$$

9. $f(x) = 2\cos 3x$

$f'(x) = -6\sin 3x, \quad f'\left(\dfrac{\pi}{2}\right) = -6\sin\left(\dfrac{3\pi}{2}\right)$

$$= -6 \times -1$$

$$= 6$$

10. General equation of a circle is $x^2 + y^2 - 2gx + 2fy + c = 0$

Centre $= (-g, -f)$

$x^2 + y^2 - 6x + 8y = 0, \qquad 2g = -6 \Rightarrow -g = 3$

$\qquad\qquad\qquad\qquad\qquad\qquad 2f = 6 \Rightarrow -f = -4$

$(-g, -f) \Rightarrow$ centre $= (3, -4)$

$\qquad\qquad C_1 \rightarrow C_2$ under reflection in x-axis

$\qquad\qquad\qquad \Rightarrow (3, -4) \rightarrow (3, 4)$

$C_2 = (3, 4) \qquad -g = 3 \Rightarrow 2g = -6$

$\qquad\qquad\qquad -f = 4 \Rightarrow 2f = -8$

Equation of circle under reflection in x-axis $= x^2 + y^2 - 6x - 8y = 0$

11.

$y = 2\log_5(2x + 5)$
At B, $x = 0$
$y = 2\log_5(0 + 5)$
$y = 2\log_5(5)$
$y = 2 \times 1 = 2$
coordinates of B(0, 2)

$y = 2\log_5(2x + 5)$
At C, $y = 4$
$y = 2\log_5(2x + 5) = 4$
$2\log_5(2x + 5) = 2$
$5^2 = 2x + 5$
$2x + 5 = 25$
$2x = 20; x = 10$
coordinates of C(10, 4)

$y = 2\log_5(2x + 5)$
At A, $y = 0$
$2\log_5(2x + 5) = 0$
$\log_5(2x + 5)^2 = 0$
$5^0 = (2x + 5)^2$
$(2x + 5)^2 = 1$
$2x + 5 = 1$
$2x = -4; x = -2$
coordinates of A(−2, 0)

12. $\cos ABC = \dfrac{BA \cdot BC}{|BA||BC|}$

If AB is perpendicular to BC
then BA . BC = 0

$BA = a - b$
$BC = c - b$

$$\begin{array}{cc} a & - & b \\ \begin{bmatrix} 3 \\ -1 \\ 0 \end{bmatrix} & - & \begin{bmatrix} 2 \\ 0 \\ 1 \end{bmatrix} = \begin{bmatrix} 1 \\ -1 \\ -1 \end{bmatrix} \end{array} \qquad \begin{array}{cc} c & - & b \\ \begin{bmatrix} 1 \\ 1 \\ -1 \end{bmatrix} & - & \begin{bmatrix} 2 \\ 0 \\ 1 \end{bmatrix} = \begin{bmatrix} -1 \\ 1 \\ -2 \end{bmatrix} \end{array}$$

$BA \cdot BC = (1 \times -1) + (-1 \times 1) + (-1 \times -2) = -1 + -1 + 2 = 0$

Since $BA \cdot BC = 0$, BA is perpendicular to BC, and angle ABC = 90°.

WORKED EXAMPLE — TEST PAPER L

1.
$$x^2 + 100 = x^2 - 100 + 200$$

$$\frac{x^2 + 100}{x + 10} = \frac{(x + 10)(x - 10) + 200}{x + 10} = x - 10 + \frac{200}{x + 10}$$

$$k = 200$$

2. If the points are collinear, then lines are parallel.

Hence $\overrightarrow{AB} = k\overrightarrow{BC}$

A(3, −1), B(a, 2), C(b, 5)

$$\boldsymbol{a} = \begin{pmatrix} 3 \\ -1 \end{pmatrix}, \; \boldsymbol{b} = \begin{pmatrix} a \\ 2 \end{pmatrix}, \; \boldsymbol{c} = \begin{pmatrix} b \\ 5 \end{pmatrix}$$

$$\overrightarrow{AB} = \boldsymbol{b} - \boldsymbol{a} = \begin{pmatrix} a - 3 \\ 3 \end{pmatrix}, \overrightarrow{BC} = \begin{pmatrix} b - a \\ 3 \end{pmatrix}$$

$$\Rightarrow \quad a - 3 = b - a$$
$$\Rightarrow \quad 2a = b + 3$$
$$\Rightarrow \quad 2a - b = 3$$

<u>Alternative Method</u>

A(3, −1), B(a, 2), C(b, 5)

If points are collinear then gradient of AB = gradient of BC.

$$m_{AB} = \frac{3}{a - 3} . \; m_{BC} = \frac{3}{b - a}$$

$$\Rightarrow \quad \frac{3}{a - 3} = \frac{3}{b - a}$$

$$\Rightarrow \quad a - 3 = b - a$$
$$\Rightarrow \quad 2a = 3 + b$$
$$\Rightarrow \quad 2a - b = 3$$

3. $K = 3 \cos \left(3x - \dfrac{\pi}{2} \right), \qquad 0 \le x \le 2\pi$

maximum value $= 3$ when $\cos \left(3x - \dfrac{\pi}{2} \right) = 1$

$\cos 0 = 1, \; \cos 2\pi = 1, \; \cos 4\pi = 1$

$$\Rightarrow \left(3x - \frac{\pi}{2} \right) = 0, \; 2\pi \text{ or } 4\pi$$

$$\Rightarrow \quad 3x = 0 + \frac{\pi}{2}, \; 2\pi + \frac{\pi}{2} \text{ or } 4\pi + \frac{\pi}{2}$$

$$\Rightarrow \quad 3x = \frac{\pi}{2}, \; \frac{5\pi}{2} \text{ or } \frac{9\pi}{6}$$

$$\Rightarrow \quad x = \frac{\pi}{6}, \; \frac{5\pi}{6} \text{ or } \frac{3\pi}{2}$$

minimum value $= -3$ when $\cos\left(3x - \dfrac{\pi}{2}\right) = -1$

$\cos \pi = -1, \ \cos 3\pi = -1, \ \cos 5\pi = -1$

$\Rightarrow \quad \left(3x - \dfrac{\pi}{2}\right) = \pi, \ 3\pi, \ 5\pi$

$\Rightarrow \quad 3x = \pi + \dfrac{\pi}{2}, \ 3\pi + \dfrac{\pi}{2}, \ 5\pi + \dfrac{\pi}{2}$

$\Rightarrow \quad 3x = \dfrac{3\pi}{2}, \ \dfrac{7\pi}{2}, \ \dfrac{11\pi}{2}$

$\Rightarrow \quad x = \dfrac{\pi}{2}, \ \dfrac{7\pi}{6} \ \dfrac{11\pi}{6}$

solution set $\left\{\dfrac{\pi}{6}, \dfrac{\pi}{2}, \dfrac{5\pi}{6}, \dfrac{7\pi}{6}, \dfrac{3\pi}{2}, \dfrac{11\pi}{6}\right\}$

or coordinates are $\left(\dfrac{\pi}{6}, +3\right), \left(\dfrac{\pi}{2}, -3\right), \left(\dfrac{5\pi}{6}, +3\right), \left(\dfrac{7\pi}{6}, -3\right), \left(\dfrac{3\pi}{2}, +3\right), \left(\dfrac{11\pi}{6}, -3\right)$

4. $\quad 2\cos 2x - 1 = 0$

$\quad\quad 2\cos 2x \ = 1$

$\quad\quad \cos 2x \ = \dfrac{1}{2}$

$\quad\quad\quad\quad\quad = 0 \cdot 5$

$\cos^{-1}(0 \cdot 5) = 60$ in quadrant 1 and $(360 - 60)$ in quadrant 4

$\quad\quad 2x \ = 60° \text{ or } 300°$

$\quad\quad x \ = 30° \text{ or } 150°$

Period of $\cos 2x = \dfrac{360}{2} = 180°$ (i.e., 2 cycles in 360°) add 180 to 30 and 150.

Hence, x has 4 possible values, 30°, 150°, 210° and 330°.

5. $\quad f(x) = 0 \ \Rightarrow \ x(x^2 + 4)(x^2 - 3)(x^2 - 1) = 0$

$\quad\quad\quad\quad\quad\quad \Rightarrow \ x = 0, \ x = \pm\sqrt{3}, \ x = \pm\sqrt{1}$

$\quad\quad\quad\quad\quad\quad\quad \text{S.S. } \{-\sqrt{3}, -1, 0, 1, \sqrt{3}\}$

Note: $x^2 + 4 = 0 \Rightarrow x^2 = -4$

No real solution, $x \notin R$.

6. $f(x) = x^3 + 3x^2 - 4x + q$

If $(x - 2)$ is a factor of $f(x)$

Then $f(2) = 0$

By synthetic division

$$
\begin{array}{c|cccc}
 & x^3 & + 3x^2 & - 4x & + q \\
 & 1 & 3 & -4 & q \\
2 & & 2 & 10 & 12 \\
\hline
 & 1 & 5 & 6 & 12 + q
\end{array}
$$

$12 + q \Rightarrow 12 + q = 0,$

$q = -12$

$f(x) = x^3 + 3x^2 - 4x - 12$

7. $P(-1, 5), Q(-3, 2), R(9, -1)$

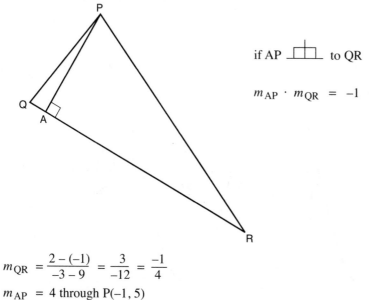

if AP ⊥ to QR

$m_{AP} \cdot m_{QR} = -1$

$m_{QR} = \dfrac{2 - (-1)}{-3 - 9} = \dfrac{3}{-12} = \dfrac{-1}{4}$

$m_{AP} = 4$ through $P(-1, 5)$

$y - 5 = 4(x + 1)$

$y - 5 = 4x + 4 \Rightarrow y = 4x + 9$ equation of altitude AP.

8. *(a)* $u_{r+1} = Ku_r + t, \ u_0 = 2, \ u_1 = -2, \ u_2 = 10$

$u_1 = Ku_0 + t \Rightarrow -2 = (2)K + t$ ①

$u_2 = Ku_1 + t \Rightarrow 10 = (-2)K + t$ ②

Add $\Rightarrow 8 = 2t, \ t = 4$

Substitute $t = 4$ in ①, $-2 = 2K + t \Rightarrow 2K + 4$

$\Rightarrow 2K = -6$

$K = -3$

$u_{r+1} = Ku_r + t, \ K = -3, \ t = 4$

$u_{r+1} = -3u_r + 4$

(b) To find $u_{r+1} = u_r \Rightarrow -3u_r + 4 = u_r$

$\Rightarrow 4u_r = 4$

$\Rightarrow u_r = 1$

Test $u_1 = 1, \ u_{r+1} = -3(1) + 4 = 1$

85

9. $f(x) = 3\cos 2x$ max $= 3$ when $2x = 0, 2\pi, 4\pi$

$$x = 0, \pi, 2\pi$$

min $= -3$ when $2x = \pi, 3\pi$

$$x = \frac{\pi}{2}, \frac{3\pi}{2}$$

x-intercept, $\cos 2x = 0$, $2x \; \frac{n\pi}{2}$ (for n odd)

$$2x = \frac{\pi}{2}, \frac{3\pi}{2}, \frac{5\pi}{2}, \frac{7\pi}{2}$$

$$x = \frac{\pi}{4}, \frac{3\pi}{4}, \frac{5\pi}{4}, \frac{7\pi}{4}$$

Points to plot:

$$(0, 3), \left(\frac{\pi}{4}, 0\right), \left(\frac{\pi}{2}, -3\right), \left(\frac{3\pi}{4}, 0\right), (\pi, 3), \left(\frac{5\pi}{4}, 0\right), \left(\frac{3\pi}{2}, -3\right), \left(\frac{7\pi}{4}, 0\right), (2\pi, 3)$$

10. *(a)* $f(x) = ax^2 + 4x - 2$ discriminant $b^2 - 4ac$

For equal roots $b^2 - 4ac = 0$

$$a = a, \; b = 4, \; c = -2$$

$$b^2 - 4ac = 16 - 4(a)(-2)$$

$$\Rightarrow \quad 16 + 8a = 0$$

$$8a = -16$$

$$a = -2$$

y-intercept $(0, -2)$, x-intercept $(1, 0)$

$$\frac{-b \pm \sqrt{0}}{2a} \qquad a = -2$$

$$= \frac{-4}{-4} = 1$$

$-2x^2$, shape

(b) $f(x)$ has real roots if $b^2 - 4ac > 0$

$\Rightarrow 16 + 8a > 0$

$8a > -16$

$a > -2$

(c) $f(x)$ has real roots if $b^2 - 4ac < 0$

$\Rightarrow 16 + 8a < 0$

$8a < -16$

$a < -2$

(d)

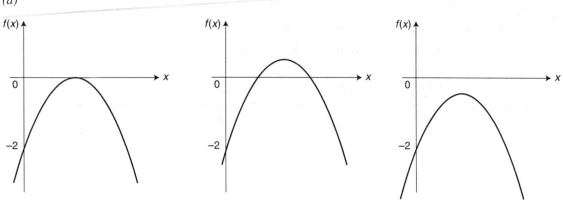

equal roots   real roots   no real roots

11. *(a)* Find the equation of the tangent to the curve $y = x^3 - 4x^2 + 2x$ at the point where $x = 1$.

The point of contact is $(1, f(1)) = (1, -1)$

$$f(x) = x^3 - 4x^2 + 2x$$

$$\text{gradient} = f'(x) = 3x^2 - 8x + 2$$

$$\text{gradient} = f'(1) = 3(1)^2 - 8(1) + 2$$

$$= -3$$

$$m = -3 \text{ through } (1, -1)$$

$$y - b = m(x - a)$$

$$y - (-1) = -3(x - 1)$$

$$y + 1 = -3x + 3$$

$$y + 3x = 2 \text{ is the required equation.}$$

(b) $y + 3x = 2$; when $x = 0$, $y = 2$; when $y = 0$, $3x = 2$, $x = \dfrac{2}{3}$

coordinates are $(0, 2)$ and $\left(\dfrac{2}{3}, 0\right)$

12. A = (−1, 4, −2), B = (1, 2, −3) and C = (0, 3, −4),

$$\cos BAC = \frac{AB \cdot AC}{|AB||AC|}$$

AB = $\mathbf{b}$ − $\mathbf{a}$

AC = $\mathbf{c}$ − $\mathbf{a}$

$$\begin{array}{cc} \mathbf{b} - \mathbf{a} & \mathbf{c} - \mathbf{a} \end{array}$$

$$\begin{bmatrix} 1 \\ 2 \\ -3 \end{bmatrix} - \begin{bmatrix} -1 \\ 4 \\ -2 \end{bmatrix} = \begin{bmatrix} 2 \\ -2 \\ -1 \end{bmatrix} \qquad \begin{bmatrix} 0 \\ 3 \\ -4 \end{bmatrix} - \begin{bmatrix} -1 \\ 4 \\ -2 \end{bmatrix} = \begin{bmatrix} 1 \\ -1 \\ -2 \end{bmatrix}$$

$BA \cdot BC = (2 \times 1) + (-2 \times -1) + (-1 \times -2) = 2 + 2 + 2 = 6$

$|AB|^2 = 2^2 + (-2)^2 + (-1)^2 = 9; \qquad |AB| = 3$

$|AC|^2 = 1^2 + (-1)^2 + (-2)^2 = 6; \qquad |AC| = \sqrt{6}$

$$\cos BAC = \frac{AB \cdot AC}{|AB||AC|} = \frac{6}{3 \times \sqrt{6}} = \frac{2}{\sqrt{6}} \text{ as given.}$$

Since the cosine of angle BAC is positive, the angle is in the first quadrant and is an acute angle.

Printed by Bell & Bain Ltd., Glasgow, Scotland, U.K.